How to Decide

A guide for women

Nelle Tumlin Scholz
Coordinator, Career Counseling Center, University of Georgia, Athens, Georgia

Judith Sosebee Prince
Director of Counseling, Office of Student Affairs, Wesleyan College, Macon, Georgia

Gordon Porter Miller
Program Service Officer, Decision-Making Program, College Entrance Examination Board

College Entrance Examination Board, New York, 1975

The College Entrance Examination Board is a nonprofit membership organization that provides tests and other educational services for students, schools, and colleges. The membership is composed of more than 2,000 colleges, schools, school systems, and education associations. Representatives of the members serve on the Board of Trustees and advisory councils and committees that consider the Board's programs and participate in the determination of its policies and activities.

Copies of this book may be ordered from College Board Publication Orders, Box 2815, Princeton, New Jersey 08540. The price is $5.95.

Editorial inquiries concerning this book should be directed to Editorial Office, College Entrance Examination Board, 888 Seventh Avenue, New York, New York 10019.

Library of Congress Catalog Card Number: 75-35474

Printed in the United States of America.

Contents

Acknowledgments

How to Decide: A Guide for Women grew out of a concern for and an attempt to meet the needs of women with whom we have worked over the years. We gratefully acknowledge those women who have shared their lives and decisions with us and whose enthusiasm, support, and contributions of ideas and personal case histories helped make this book possible.

We acknowledge the members of the 1973-74 Parthenian Chapter of Mortar Board at the University of Georgia who worked with the first two authors in developing materials for a peer-counseling program on career decision-making for college women, some adaptations of which have been incorporated in this book. Subsequent Mortar Board chapters at the University of Georgia and at Wesleyan College have contributed their ideas as they have used the materials in peer-counseling sessions.

We wish to acknowledge the influence of Patricia Jakubowski-Spector's workshops and concepts in developing the section on assertiveness as a strategy. We wish to thank H. B. Gelatt, Barbara Varenhorst, and Richard Carey for their pioneering work in the field of decision-making, which served as the springboard for this publication. We are indebted to Anne Marsden, a career intern from Colgate University, for her very useful research. Our thanks also to the College Entrance Examination Board, especially Patricia A. Wyatt, Program Service Officer for the Decision-Making Program, for her many helpful suggestions for improving the manuscript; and Marcia Van Meter, Managing Editor, for her expert editorial assistance.

A special word of appreciation goes to our families who felt that our decision to spend time on this book was a good one.

N.T.S.
J.S.P.
G.P.M.

Foreword

How to Decide
A guide for women

is about a difficult subject: learning how to make decisions. Making decisions is not easy for most people, especially when those decisions are important to the individual involved. Yet our world of change and uncertainty demands that we make choices, and good ones. Women, especially, have experienced rather rapid change in society; new freedoms, new roles, new values have offered new possibilities to women and have created new needs for them as well. This book is designed to meet the changing needs of women by increasing their decision-making ability and by helping them apply the dynamics of decision-making to planning their lives in a world of broadening and different opportunities and expectations. In addition, *How to Decide* seeks to develop a broader concept of women's roles and emerging life patterns, to awaken women to the spectrum of new possibilities opening to them, and to serve as a catalyst for purposeful planning by women.

How to Decide is appropriate for women of all ages, from college through retirement, but it is especially appropriate for women who are trying to make their lives more constructive and satisfying.

The exercises and activities in this book are generally drawn from actual life experiences, and they will be most helpful to readers who become actively involved and complete a wide variety of them. *How to Decide: A Guide for Women* has been used effectively in both individual and group settings.

The authors will welcome any comments or suggestions readers might have regarding any aspect of this book.

Where are you as a Woman?

What, then, might the American woman become? Who can she be? Who will she be? We might become whatever we want to become, whatever we have the wisdom, the strength, the courage, and the fortitude to become. We can be whoever we choose to be. We will be whoever we develop ourselves into being.

M. Louise McBee and *Kathryn A. Blake, 1974*

"Helmer: Before all else you are a wife and mother."

"Nora: That I no longer believe. I believe that before all else I am a human being. Just as you are—or at least that I should try to become one."

Henrik Ibsen, 1879

"A woman should be seen, not heard."

Sophocles

"Woman's destiny is not just to be attractive, to be able to find a smart, rich husband, and to be a good housewife and mother. She can be all of these if she chooses to be. But first and foremost she is a person, and she should be treated like one. As a person, she also has the responsibility to acquire maximum potential and self-actualization. The process of defining herself and her identity is her own responsibility and should not be exclusively dictated by society and its expectations, although society can set some guidelines."

Vijay Sharma, 1974

"I do pray, and that most honestly and consistently, for some terrific shock to startle the women of the nation into a self-respect which will compel them to see the absolute degradation of their present position; which will compel them to break their yoke or bondage and give them faith in themselves; which will make them proclaim their allegiance to women. . . . The fact is, women are in chains and their servitude is all the more debasing because they do not realize it. O to compel them to see and feel and to give them the courage and consciousness to speak and act for their own freedom, though they face the scorn and contempt of all the world for doing it!"

Susan B. Anthony, 1872

"I'd like to see the day when a mediocre woman can go as far as a mediocre man."

Bernice Sandler, 1972

"A woman is to be from her house three times: when she is baptized, when she is married, and when she is buried."

Thomas Fuller, 1732

"Woman may be said to be an inferior man."

Aristotle

"Not all women want to be astronauts, but neither do all women want to be housewives and/or secretaries."

Impact, 1974

"A bright woman is caught in a double bind. In testing and other achievement-oriented situations she worries not only about failure, but also about success. If she fails, she is not living up to her own standards of performance; if she succeeds she is not living up to societal expectations about the female role."

Matina Horner, 1969

"But even if all discrimination were to end tomorrow, nothing very drastic would change. For job discrimination is only part of the problem. It does impede women who choose to become lawyers or managers or physicians. But it does not, by itself, help us understand why so many women 'choose' to be secretaries or nurses rather than executives or physicians. That 'something' is an unconscious ideology about the nature of the female sex, an ideology which constricts the emerging self-image of the female child and the nature of her aspirations from the very first. . . . The "homogenization" of America's women is the major consequence of our sex-role ideology."

Sandra L. Bem and *Daryl J. Bem, 1973*

If you don't decide, you've made a choice

Making decisions is commonplace for all of us. Some of us make them more consciously and systematically than others. Some of us have confidence in our skills in decision-making, and others find it difficult to make even the most trivial choices. Some people are not aware of many of the choices they could make, and some feel better letting others make choices for them.

Regardless of how you make choices or how you feel about making choices, your decisions determine your future. A decision is an act, and in taking or choosing a specific action, an individual is required to make a commitment of personal resources that cannot be replaced. The resources committed might involve time, money, a personal relationship, a career, a style of life, or even a strongly held belief. A decision might be painful, pleasant, or anxiety-producing, or it might relieve a troubling situation. A decision can be and do all these things, but most of all it means taking action. It means getting off the fence. It can be a way to move you toward what you want or what is important to you and give you control and freedom over your life.

In today's world and in the future everyone will be called on to make more choices as changes evolve in an advanced technological society. Perhaps no one will be more aware of the implications of increased options than the American woman who is exploring and testing new roles and opportunities that heretofore have been unavailable to her or that she has found unacceptable. The woman of today has been thrust into a new set of conditions that have great implications for her personal, educational, and career life. As is true for anyone facing new and important choices, this situation is likely to cause anxieties. Although the freedom to choose may be clearly apparent to a person, the ability to choose may not be so apparent.

Indeed, most people, men or women, old or young, have had little help in learning how to make well-informed, well-considered choices.

The problem of acquiring skill in making decisions is especially acute for women. Many women are not aware of the choices open to them. They may feel anxious, confused, uneasy, or frustrated because their experiences have not prepared them for deciding. And even when they have learned how to make effective decisions they may not be able to take action unless others approve. A woman who is anxious about the very notion of making a decision is hardly in a position to take advantage of newly available options relating to her education, her career, and her life.

It is the purpose of this book to help women learn decision-making skills so that any uncertainties they may have about making choices can be reduced and any anxiety they may associate with decision-making can be lessened. The decision-making process you will follow in these pages can apply to any decision, whether it is personal or whether it relates to your career. The word "career" as used in this book refers to lifelong learning, living, and working experiences. The book is intended to help you learn to use what you know to get what you want out of life, whether you are a student, a business executive, a housewife, an artist, a mother—or some combination of these.

In other words, this book is directed to you, a unique individual. It is based on the idea that people who learn to decide effectively can direct their lives effectively. It can help you to focus on what is really important to you, it can teach you how to evaluate and use information in making your decisions, it can provide you with some techniques by which you can identify and explore new alternatives—and it can encourage

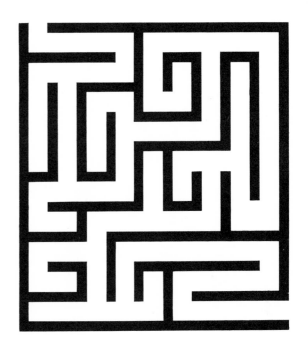

you to take action. Like many others who have learned to use the decision-making process, you may find greater freedom in your life and learn ways to develop greater control over what you do and what you plan to do in the future.

A good beginning in gaining greater freedom of choice and control over your life is to examine some of your attitudes toward yourself and toward other women and what effect these attitudes are having on you. For example, what do you think a woman should be? How binding or important to you are some of the stereotypes about women? The self-evaluation in the following pages can help you confront your image of appropriate "feminine" behavior.

What

What people think of themselves, as well as what others think of them, has a great deal to do with what decisions they make. Sometimes your perception of yourself may be inaccurate, and sometimes your perception of what others might think of you may also be inaccurate. If you get things out where you can examine them, you will probably find them easier to deal with. The statements listed below sum up some common attitudes and ideas, things many people seem to believe. As you go down the list check the ones you believe are essentially true.

Women as Workers

_____More women would work if their husbands would encourage it.

_____Women handle routine, detailed, repetitive work better than creative imaginative tasks.

_____Women who work are taking jobs away from men.

_____Women prefer working for a male boss.

_____Women have a responsibility to put their talents to work outside the home.

_____A college degree is a waste of money for women if they never expect to use it through gainful employment.

Women as Wives and Mothers

_____A woman who works full time cannot possibly be as good a mother to her grade school children as one who stays home.

_____A woman's first responsibility is to be a companion to her husband and a mother.

_____Husbands who feel threatened by a careerist wife are unsure of their masculinity.

_____Women have lost their own identity when they have to derive their only status from their husbands.

_____The man is the head of the household.

_____Every woman is looking for a prince, a man to take care of her.

_____The only place for a woman is in the home.

Women as Persons

_____Women tend to respond emotionally; men respond intellectually.

_____Women have less need to achieve than men in the working world.

_____Women tend to feel inadequate. Instead of using their mistakes for growth, they use them as justification for dropping out, for quitting, or for putting the blame on someone else.

_____Women's image in the mass media overly emphasizes beauty, fashions, or homemaking values.

_____Women do not want full equality if it means equal responsibility.

_____Women are by nature more mediating and cooperative than men.

keeps you from deciding?

Women as Decision–Makers

_____Women tend to make decisions intuitively, not rationally.

_____Women are not permitted to make important decisions; society or their families make decisions for them.

_____Women are too emotional to make well-informed, well-considered decisions.

_____Women tend to let others—husbands, parents, friends—make decisions for them.

_____Women lack conviction; they do not stick up for their choices.

Look back over the list at the statements you have checked as representing essentially what you think. Have some of these beliefs affected your decisions? If you think they have, can you identify the ones that may have been serious obstacles to your going after what you want? Put an "M" next to the statements that are the most serious obstacles to your making a decision. Put an "L" next to those that are the least serious.

Have any of the above beliefs affected a recent decision you have made? If so, give an example: _____

_____

_____

_____

_____

_____

Are there other statements you believe or others believe about women that have affected your role as a decision-maker? What are they? _____

_____

_____

_____

_____

_____

Most women responding to these statements find several in each category that have affected their decision-making or their ability to take action to move toward what they want. Others find whole categories relating to how they direct their lives. The category "Women as Decision-Makers" is the one that many women find to be the most difficult to deal with. How do you make a decision and then have the courage to stand up for it?

If you feel that way or find obstacles in any of the above categories, you're not unlike a lot of people who are trying to make their lives more satisfying, and this book should be helpful to you.

Sometimes in learning to make decisions it's useful to examine how other people have handled their lives. In the following pages you'll have an opportunity to observe and study how others have dealt with critical decisions in their lives. As a starting point, read about Marlene. While you are observing her situation, try to ascertain how the statements you have just read may have affected Marlene's role as a woman, her life plans, and her decisions.

Marlene: What's important?

Marlene is a college student. She attended a lecture on the changing role of women and felt confused by some of the things she heard:

- Of the nearly 32 million women who work in the United States almost 3 out of 5 are married.

- Women have always had jobs; they have rarely been permitted careers.

- Fewer than 1 percent of all women workers are in "professional" positions such as physician, lawyer, scientist, editor, or senator.

- If you elect not to work, not to enter a profession, or if you elect to stay home—that's your business.

- People are different, and therefore they should make different choices.

Marlene had always thought she would marry, have a home, and raise children as her mother had done, that this was the major purpose of her life. A career outside her home would be incidental, a remote possibility. Now she was wondering what would best satisfy her.

Did she really want to be like her mother? Lately, Marlene had detected some feelings of dissatisfaction in her mother, perhaps even resentment that her husband and children were taking her for granted. What would cause her to feel that way? Her mother had graduated from college, taught school for two years, and then married a man who provided a good living for her and their three children. Apprehensively, Marlene questioned her own plans for the future. Whom would she marry, or did she want to marry? Did she want a career? Could she marry and have a career too?

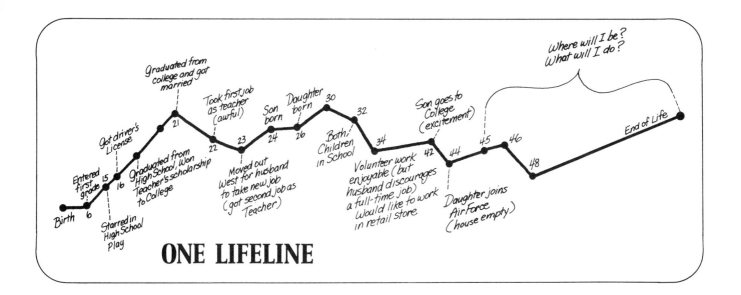

ONE LIFELINE

Nobody had ever really encouraged Marlene to think about what career she would like. She had been told that she might consider being an art teacher, that this would be a good choice for a woman. But she did not want to be an art teacher. She wanted to be an architect. She wanted to draw house plans, not pictures. But would she ever finish that? All her friends would be married before she even finished school—and she thought she wanted to get married. Why not go ahead and major in art education and then, after she married, if she still wanted to be an architect maybe she could go back to school.

"Certainly," Marlene thought, "I must have more decisions to make than my mother ever did." She drifted from one decision to another. One day it was like this; the next it was that. Occasionally she felt confident, but generally she felt lost and without direction. She couldn't make a decision she could stick to because she wasn't sure what she wanted.

Write in your answers to these questions about Marlene:

Why is Marlene confused? _____

_____

_____

Have you been asking yourself some of the questions Marlene is considering? Have they affected your thinking? _____

_____

_____

Will considering the life of her mother be helpful or not helpful to Marlene as she begins to consider a plan for her life? Why?

Helpful: _____

_____

_____

Not helpful: _____

_____

_____

Marlene's mother may be typical of many women who think about the future in a general way without considering what their decisions about job, marriage, and family may mean to them personally 5, 10, or 15 years later. How can Marlene avoid a similar predicament? _____

_____

_____

_____

What will your lifeline be like?

Women follow varied life patterns, some the traditional family pattern followed by Marlene's mother, working only after formal education, some a single person's pattern in which work assumes a significant part of life, and some a dichotomous career-family pattern of work with only brief leaves for having children. Most women tend to fall statistically close to the pattern of Marlene's mother: first child born at age 26, last child born at 29, and the last child entering school at age 35. Consider the life pattern drawn in the box at the top of this page. What does it tell you? Do you think of your life as having ups and downs like these, as having a shape? Does it seem familiar? Why? _____

_____

_____

_____

_____

In the spaces below, draw a lifeline for a woman you know well, perhaps your mother or a close friend, and a lifeline for yourself. Each line can have its own shape, but each should begin at a point you consider to be the beginning of the life and terminate where you consider the end of the life to be. Write in the events that shape the lifelines you draw. After you have plotted your lifeline to where you are today, continue shaping it by projecting how you would like it to look in the future.

The lifeline of a woman you know well:

Your lifeline:

Most lifelines are different, or at least they're shaped by different events and different actions or decisions. What decisions made the lifelines you've drawn above different? How many of the actions that shaped your own lifeline resulted from choices you made, and how many from choices others made for you? Is there evidence of action you've taken without really making a decision—that is, something you did simply because it was expected of you?

How your decisions affect your lifeline

Once again draw a lifeline for yourself, but don't write in your age or the events that shaped the line.

Now put the following symbols along your lifeline. Put (!) where you took the greatest risk of your life. Place (X) where you encountered an obstacle preventing you from getting or doing what you wanted. Use (O) to locate a critical decision that was made for you by someone else. Put (+) at the point of the best decision you've ever made and (−) at the worst decision you've made. Finally put (?) where you see a critical or important decision coming up in the future. It might be helpful to describe what each symbol represents.

Consider your lifeline carefully now, complete with symbols. Have you learned anything that surprises you? _____

_____

_____

How have decisions affected the shape of your lifeline? _____

_____

_____

Did you actually make the decisions that affected your life? _____

Learning to Decide

Most people have had little practice in learning and applying decision-making skills, and yet everyone is constantly being told or asked to decide. Practice in learning and applying decision-making skills might help you with some of your problems.

A good way to reduce the number of difficulties you might experience in making decisions is to learn some of the things that are involved in this process. Consider the statements in italic type below and try to respond to the questions following them.

A decision is the act of a person in choosing, selecting, or deciding among several possibilities.

Write down an important decision you face right now: _____

_____

_____

What makes this decision important?

_____

_____

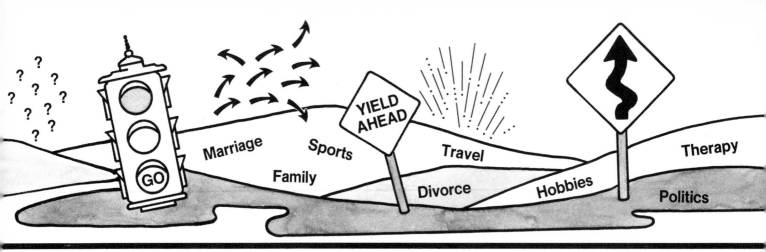

A decision can be rated as critical or important if it has something to do with what you can or cannot do in the future, if it affects others, if it is important to you, if it is difficult to resolve immediately.

A decision is not possible unless there are two or more courses of action to take.

What are the alternatives (actions you can take) related to the decision you listed on page 11?

_____
_____
_____

An outcome is the result, consequence, or aftermath of a person's action or decision.

What outcomes, good and bad, can you predict for each of the alternatives you listed above?

_____
_____
_____

It is the individual who makes each decision unique. Two individuals may face a similar decision, but each person is different, and each may want a different outcome.

Write down a poor decision you have made:

_____
_____

Why do you consider it to be a poor decision?

_____
_____
_____

Most people say that a decision is poor if the result was not what they wanted; however, a person has direct control over the decision, not

the outcome. A good decision does not guarantee a good outcome, because you cannot control the outcome. A good decision will increase your chances of having a good outcome.*

What is a good decision you have made?

_____
_____

Why was it good? _____

_____
_____
_____

A good decision is one in which the skills of decision-making are used to choose the alternative that is best according to the decision-maker's preference. The "goodness" of a decision is based on how it is made, not on how it turns out. A good decision could yield a bad outcome, and a bad decision (one poorly made) could yield a good outcome.

What is a career decision?

A career consists of those major activities, related or not related to work, which are of prime importance during one's life. Any decision you feel is important (critical) enough to include on your lifeline may be a career decision for you.

In sum, decision-making is a lifelong process. It should help you to:

Recognize and define the decisions that will determine what the rest of your life will be. Career planning is a continuous process. You have been and will be making many decisions relevant to career plans—decisions about a college major, about summer work experiences,

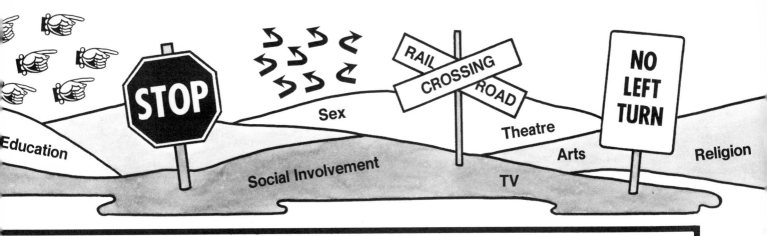

about marriage, about finding a job, about retirement, about having children, and about your life goals.

Know yourself—what is important to you, what you can do, and what you want to accomplish. To understand yourself as a unique person and as a woman, you need to examine your attitudes toward the role of women, recognize any conflicting values you may have, explore the values you have relating to work, and establish short-range and long-range objectives. Your experiences can provide you with knowledge of your abilities, aptitudes, and interests.

Evaluate the information you already have —and seek, evaluate, and use new information. For example, if you are making decisions about an occupation, you must know something about opportunities and limitations in the fields you are considering. You need information about supply and demand for particular occupations, job characteristics, skills required, and education necessary. You need to be able to assess the risks and costs involved in the alternatives that are available.

Develop a plan of action or strategy for attaining what you want. Learning decision-making skills will be useful in formulating a plan of action that relates what you consider to be important to the options that are available.

Develop skills that will help you overcome the obstacles women face in attempting to implement new life plans or change undesirable existing characteristics or conditions. Decision-making skills are learned and can be applied to all your important choices, whether they involve personal, educational, or occupational matters.

 CHECKPOINT

Do you know where you stand as a woman? Write a statement that summarizes your basic feelings or thoughts with regard to yourself as a woman in today's world. _____

_____
_____
_____

Before going on, you might find it helpful to consider the following questions.

• How confident are you that you understand yourself—your interests, values, and abilities?

• Do you want to know how to make your own decisions about your career and life and feel more confident that your decisions are good decisions?

• Can you accept responsibility for your own decisions, regardless of their outcomes?

• Can you establish or set goals for yourself?

• Do you know how to identify the barriers or obstacles that might prevent your attaining a specific goal you might set for yourself?

• Do you know where and how to find information and help to overcome these barriers or obstacles so that your goal might be reachable?

• How important is it for you to develop skills that will help you get what you want in life?

The next pages in this book deal with a very important step toward developing these skills—learning what is important to you and how important it is.

If you want to try learning more about yourself go on to the next section. It's your decision!

Who are you?

WHAT is important to you and HOW important is it?

Up to this point you have examined the kinds of general attitudes, experiences, and values that you hold or that society holds that have had something to do with the freedom and control you have had in your life, especially as it relates to getting what you want. But before you can move effectively toward what you want, it is important to discover what you know about yourself — things such as your values, abilities, interests, and special talents. Most important in this discovery process is to learn to understand yourself — what is important to you and how important it is. Learning what you value and what your value priorities are requires a great deal of thought as well as a study of your behavior. What is important to you tends to show up in what you do — what actions you take, or what decisions you make. Sometimes it is very difficult to find out what you value because people do learn new values, values change over time, and so do value priorities. So, what is important to you today may not have been important to you five years ago and may not be five years from now.

In this section you will participate in a series of activities to help you discover what is important to you and how you can use this knowledge in moving toward what you want in life. Knowing this and more about your interests, abilities, and special talents is vital if you expect to make well-considered, well-informed choices about anything.

What do you want in life?

To get an idea of how vital it is to learn what is really important to you, try the following exercise. Don't worry if it's difficult or even impossible for you to respond to some of these questions. If you can't respond now, you can come back as you learn more about yourself and complete the exercise.

Write down three things you want most in life:

1. _____

2. _____

3. _____

Examine what you've written down. What does each thing have to do with what is important to you — what you value?

1. _____

_____

2. _____

_____

3. _____

_____

Now, try to think of actions, some things you've done recently that show you have done something to support what is important to you and that, consequently, have moved you toward what you want in life:

1. _____

_____

_____

2. _____

_____

_____

3. _____

_____

_____

After you have studied all your responses, what have you observed? Do your actions support what you say is important to you? How? _____

_____

_____

_____

Are your actions moving you toward what you want? How? _____

_____

_____

_____

If you're not satisfied with the actions you've taken, can you think of what obstacles might be preventing you from getting closer to what you want?

_____

_____

What action should you have taken? _____

_____

_____

At this point, can you think of any ways of getting around the obstacles you listed? What are they? _____

_____

_____

The following exercises are to help you discover what is important to you, what you really value.

Sharon: Using values in making a career decision

Each woman is unique because of what she values and what she reveals about her values in the decisions she makes. Values affect the "goodness" of possible alternatives, what action will be taken, what information is required to make a decision, and judgment of the outcomes.

Read over the story that follows. Try to identify what Sharon values. Then use those values (which may differ considerably from yours) in making a decision for her.

After one year at the university, Sharon feels that college is not the place for her. Her grades show her to be a good student. She feels, however, that too much money is being spent on her education. She also feels that going to college prolongs the time before she can become independent. Sharon's parents are against her leaving college. They insist that all their children get a college education. Leaving college would not totally satisfy Sharon. She still feels

the need to be someone and to do something with her life. After much deliberation, Sharon looks into a program to train people wanting to become telephone installers. Although her mother thinks women who go into the skilled trades are "unladylike" and aggressive, Sharon likes working outdoors and having a great deal of independence while she works. She would have freedom to go out on her own, to control the speed of her work, and to manage her time. As an installer, she would do a variety of things, all requiring special skills. The work would be hard but stimulating both physically and mentally. She likes being involved in physical activities, and she feels she could get great satisfaction from meeting the physical demands and the challenges the job would make on her energy and determination. At the end of the day, Sharon could carry home a feeling of accomplishment as well as good pay.

Sharon values:_____

_____

Sharon will decide to:_____

_____

If she decides to become an installer, what kinds of objections will she get from her college friends, her parents? What pressures from society might she feel?_____

_____

_____

Working in the skilled trades allows women who like outdoor or manual work and women who like independence and freedom to move about on the job to express these preferences. Average minimum wages for plumbers, carpenters, electricians, painters, and other workers in skilled trades range from $6 to $10 an hour. In many trades apprenticeships, for learning while being paid, are available.

List below some other advantages for women entering skilled trades.

_____

_____

What do you consider to be the disadvantages?_____

_____

_____

What unusual qualities might one need to make the choice you think Sharon makes?_____

_____

_____

Dream a little...

If you were free and could do any kind of work you wanted. What would it be? Dreaming, and ignoring any possible barriers, write down what you would really like to do. Be as specific as possible.

_____

_____

_____

Close your eyes for two or three minutes. Imagine that you are in the situation or occupation you have named — doctor, lawyer, secretary, homemaker, manager, explorer, engineer, social worker, professor, auditor. Where are you? Describe the setting.

_____

_____

_____

What are you doing? What other people are there? What are they doing? _____

_____

_____

_____

Did you have any special training to get where you are? What skills or abilities are required? _____

_____

_____

_____

What is especially important to you regarding what you are doing? _____

_____

_____

_____

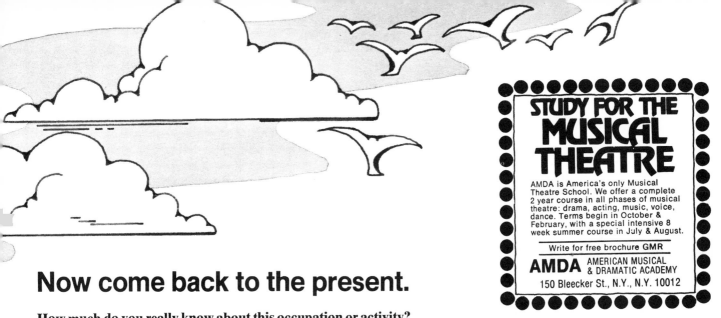

Now come back to the present.

How much do you really know about this occupation or activity?

_____

_____

What are some ways that values, interests, and abilities relate to this type of occupation?_____

_____

What alternative occupations or situations might you consider?

_____

_____

What new information do you need before choosing this occupation?_____

_____

Is what you want still a dream, or is it a possibility for you?

_____

_____

Now, try to look back 5 or 10 years. What would you have said then that you would like most to do?_____

_____

Have your values changed? If so, in what way?_____

_____

How do you feel about this change?_____

Sometimes a dream can end in a rude awakening. What is desirable and appealing may appear to be impossible. A kind of ceiling can develop over one's life preventing one from really moving toward what is desired. This ceiling is sometimes self-imposed and sometimes imposed by others. And, more often than not, it is the result of a value conflict. Conflicts can be among several things that are important to you, forcing you to give up one thing if you choose something else. Or, a conflict can be between what you think important and what others think is important. Difficult choices generally involve a value conflict. In career planning, for example, some women experience a conflict between career and marriage; others experience the conflict between being successful and being feminine; still others might feel the conflict between what they want and what others want for them.

In the story below, Kim has found that various conflicts in her life are making her choice difficult. See if you can identify some of these conflicts.

Kim is thinking about dropping out of the program for a Master of Business Administration in the middle of her first quarter. She got married in the summer to a young man working on a master's degree in art. She did well in her undergraduate major, psychology, but the courses she now has in accounting, quantitative analysis, economics, and statistics present material that is interesting but new to her. She is having to study a great deal, even at times when her new husband wants her to spend time with him. She feels that after she graduates the jobs she might get will be even more demanding on her time. She wants to have a family. She is getting more and more behind be-cause of the demands of housework and entertaining friends. She decided to major in business because of satisfying jobs she has had in retailing and office work, because she likes competition and the chances for success, and because of the availability of jobs for women in the area. She talks with her professors who encourage her to continue. One even suggests that if her husband goes into freelance art she may need to work. If she drops out, she is thinking about getting a teaching certificate so she can get jobs if her husband moves around and so she can move in and out of the world of work.

Kim:...conflicting

Describe the value conflicts Kim is experiencing: _____

_____

_____

Consider these statements:

Marriage and career do not mix.

Working is acceptable only if it does not interfere with home responsibilities.

The man should be the primary breadwinner of the family.

Women with small children should not work.

Teaching is a more practical field than business for women.

Can you identify other conflicts? _____

_____

_____

What decision do you think Kim should make? Why? _____

_____

_____

What are some values that appear important to Kim? _____

_____

_____

By making the decision you think she should make, what might be some of the results, both favorable and unfavorable, that Kim might have to face? _____

_____

_____

Describe a decision you have made in which you encountered conflicting values. Write down all the important details. _____

_____

_____

_____

How did you resolve those conflicts? _____

_____

_____

What were some of the results? _____

_____

_____

Would you do it the same way now? Why? _____

_____

values

Sometimes it's difficult to do what you want to do

Barbara is 25, single, and wants a career in banking. It is a field that offers great variety and opportunity to advance. When she graduated from college Barbara worked during the summer in a bank, but since she could not get into a training program without some graduate courses in banking she took a job as a secretary to earn enough money so she could return to college and complete a master's in business administration. As a secretary, Barbara was very successful and within three years was made an administrative assistant, which required about half secretarial duties and half time working with statistics and accounting. In spite of the fact that her boss encouraged her to stay on and even offered her an additional raise, she decided to return to college and pursue her goal of working in banking. Barbara earned her M.B.A. and began applying for positions in various commercial and savings banks. She was especially interested in trusts, investment banking, and loans, and not the administrative side of banking. At the time she

applied for jobs the opportunities were very scarce, and she received only one offer to work in a bank — a savings bank where she would be trained to be a bank manager. She was not interested in being a bank manager. Through friends and the efforts of a placement office, she was offered several jobs as a secretary, a job as an executive secretary to the president of a large corporation, and a job as a sales person in a computer firm. All the nonbanking jobs paid at least a thousand dollars more than the bank position, where the starting salary was $9,000 for the first two years. The executive secretary position paid $15,000 and the computer sales $17,500. Barbara didn't feel confident about selling, and she was reluctant to take a secretarial job, even at such a high salary, because she feared she might not be able to get into a banking position at least to try what she felt she wanted to do. Time and especially money seemed to be running out. She was living on a $500 loan, and she needed work desperately and soon.

What are some alternatives Barbara has? _____

_____

_____

_____

What do you think she decides? _____

_____

_____

Why? (What does she value?) _____

_____

_____

_____

What would you decide? Why? (What do you value?) _____

_____

_____

_____

What are the major conflicts that have to be faced in this decision situation?

_____

_____

_____

_____

To see what Barbara decides see page 24.

Considering your values in a critical decision

It is not easy to discover what is important to you, and it is even more difficult to decide what values are more important than other values and just how much more important they are. Yet, it is virtually impossible to make a well-considered choice if you don't know what is important to you and how important it is in a given decision situation. The following exercise provides a way to begin considering your values in light of a critical decision you have made or that you have to make in the future.

First make a list of all the things that are important to you. A good way to go about this is to think about things that you spend a lot of time thinking about, or things that you would like to have as part of your life. A sample list might include words like these:

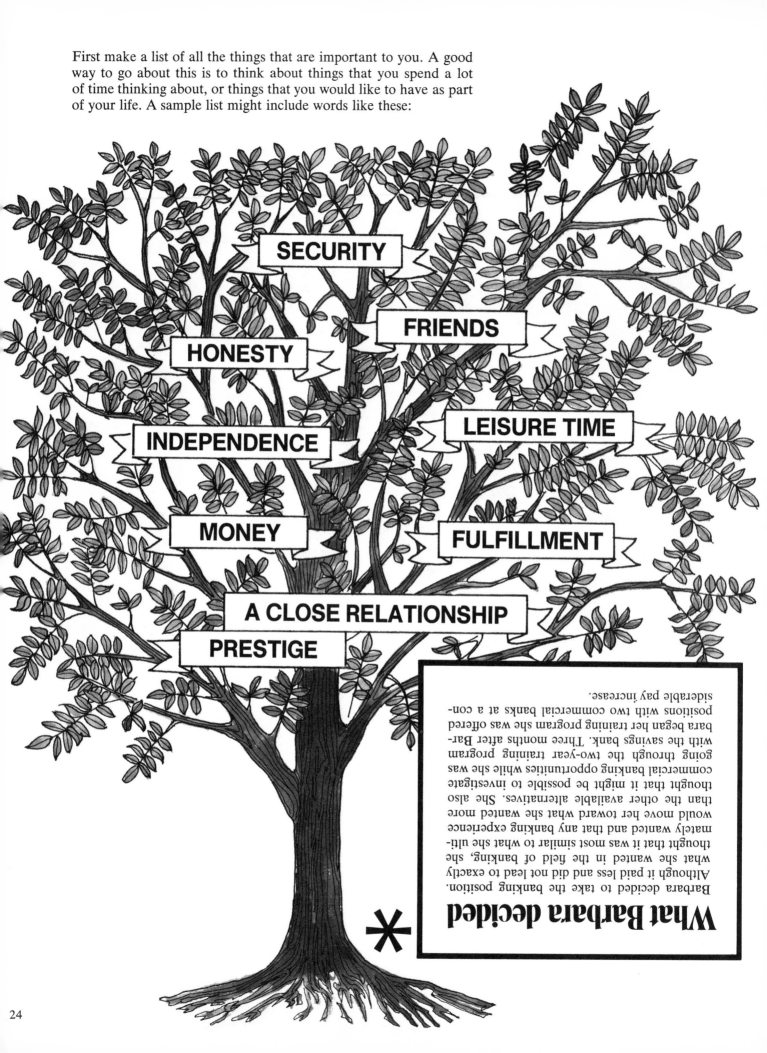

SECURITY

FRIENDS

HONESTY

LEISURE TIME

INDEPENDENCE

MONEY

FULFILLMENT

A CLOSE RELATIONSHIP

PRESTIGE

What Barbara decided

Barbara decided to take the banking position. Although it paid less and did not lead to exactly what she wanted in the field of banking, she thought that it was most similar to what she ultimately wanted and that any banking experience would move her toward what she wanted more than the other available alternatives. She also thought that it might be possible to investigate commercial banking opportunities while she was going through the two-year training program with the savings bank. Three months after Barbara began her training program she was offered positions with two commercial banks at a considerable pay increase.

In the space below, write down the values that are important to you. You may choose some from those values shown on page 24 and/or add others that you can think of.

After you have made your list, rank each of the values. Put a (1) next to the item that is most important to you, a (2) next to the item that is next most important, and so on, until each "value" you listed has a number or priority. Check your ranking by trying to relate action to your values — that is, what have you done lately that indicates that you value what you say you value?

When you have completed the list on page 25, think of an important decision you have facing you now or that you expect to face in the future. Write the decision down. Your decision might come from questions like: What shall I do with the rest of my life? What job should I take? What should I take when I return to school? As a middle-aged woman, what occupation should I pursue? What can I do to make my life more satisfying?

Your critical decision:

Why is it critical or important for you?

Now that you have identified your decision, try to think of all the alternatives, actions you might take, in this situation. List all the alternatives you can think of, including those that may not appear to be acceptable to you at this time.

_____

_____

_____

_____

_____

_____

Now list your alternatives again under Alternative 1, etc., on the lines below. Under each alternative, write all the values you listed on page 26 that this action would accommodate if you chose it. If you think of other values or of new alternatives as you're doing this exercise, feel free to add them to your lists. When you write down the value under each alternative, be sure to put the number next to it that represents its importance to you (its ranking). If your decision has to do with what to do for the rest of your life your exercise might read like this:

Alternative 1: *Enter an apprenticeship program to prepare for skilled job*

Values and their ranks: *Family (6)   Money (4)*
Honesty (1)   Prestige (9)

Alternatives, acceptable and unacceptable

Alternative 1:

Values and their ranks:

Alternative 2:

Values and their ranks:

Alternative 3:

Values and their ranks:

Alternative 4:

Values and their ranks:

Alternative 5:

Values and their ranks:

Alternative 6:

Values and their ranks:

When you have listed your values under each alternative,
look at the results and try to answer the following questions.

Which alternative accommodated the most values you listed? _____

_____

Which alternative accommodated the most important values you listed? _____

_____

Which alternative do you think is the best choice? Why? _____

_____

_____

_____

_____

_____

_____

_____

_____

ACCEPTABL

Did you learn anything new about yourself? Explain. _____

_____

_____

_____

Perhaps there are alternatives you don't know about. Think about what you might do to increase these options.

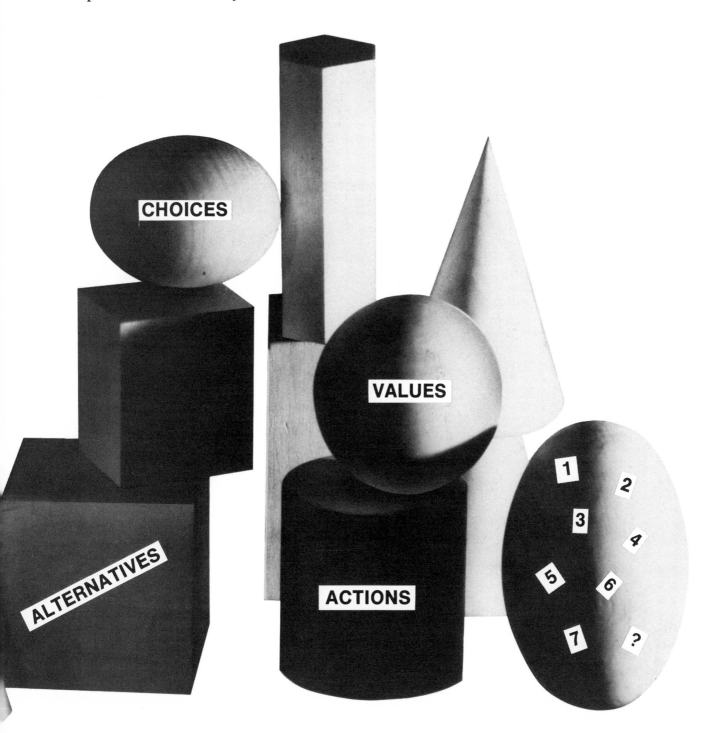

Relating your values to

Actions reveal most clearly what a person values. If you are willing to spend your time and energy doing something, or consistently choose it over something else, you are probably revealing your values. What you value has a great deal to do with the kind of work you might want to do.

Beside the numbers in the chart below write 10 things you have done during the past year. The list does not have to be in order of importance. Include paid and nonpaid activities, things you do for pleasure, things that relate to work or leisure.

On page 31 is a list of 10 common work values. Write these values in the spaces provided at the top of each successive column in the chart and then follow the directions given for each.

10 things you have done in the past year										
1.										
2.										
3.										
4.										
5.										
6.										
7.										
8.										
9.										
10.										
Total										

work

1. . . . . **INTEREST.** In the column you have labeled IN-TEREST, put a check by any activity on your list that you did because you really liked doing it. It is one of your special interests, and you find it a stimulating activity.

2. . . . . **INDEPENDENCE.** In the column you have labeled INDEPENDENCE, put a check by any activity you did because you like to do things on your own, without having a lot of orders and directions. You like the feeling of being independent.

3. . . . . **SELF-EXPRESSION.** In the column you have labeled SELF-EXPRESSION, put a check by any activity you did in any area of your abilities because you feel that using your natural talent or ability helps you express who you really are and what you do well.

4. . . . . **SERVICE.** In the column you have labeled SERVICE, put a check by any activity you did because it had meaning for others or because it was for another person's benefit. You have a need to help others, and you like to do a good and useful job wherever you are needed.

5. . . . . **LEADERSHIP.** In the column you have labeled LEADERSHIP, put a check by any activity you did because you like to use your leadership abilities. You enjoy planning and organizing a program or activity, and you get a feeling of satisfaction from knowing that you can direct and supervise the activities of others.

6. . . . . **REWARD.** In the column you have labeled REWARD, put a check by any activity you did because you expected to receive money or some other kind of reward. Perhaps you received the approval of someone significant to you or perhaps you earned a special privilege like being invited to join some select group.

7. . . . . **ACHIEVEMENT.** In the column you have labeled ACHIEVEMENT, put a check beside any activity you did because advancement and growth are important to you. You like to do things well, to do your best when you do something.

8. . . . . **RECOGNITION.** In the column you have labeled RECOGNITION, put a check beside any activity you did because recognition of your work by others is important to you. You like being respected, having prestige, and receiving approval for what you do.

9. . . . . **VARIETY.** In the column you have labeled VARIETY, put a check beside any activity you did because you like to do new and different things. You don't like routine or repetitious work.

10. . . . . **SECURITY.** In the column you have labeled SECURITY, put a check beside any activity you did because you feel comfortable doing it. You are familiar with this, and you find it easy to do.

Total: After you have checked the 10 activities for the 10 value columns, total the responses in each column on the value sheet. You can now begin to determine the strengths of your values as related to your work activities.

Write below what you have learned about yourself and your work values.

_____

_____

_____

_____

What work value emerges the most? The least? Why?

_____

_____

_____

_____

_____

_____

Values relating to work make up only part of the career an individual pursues throughout life. People generally value things in addition to work values when they talk about leisure, formal education, informal education, and personal relationships. It is this total pattern of values that we bring to bear when we make decisions relating to all aspects of our lives. And when we take certain actions, as we grow and experience new things, our values change and so do the values of the people around us. Ten years ago, it might have been considered unusual for a woman to prefer a career as a working single person over a career as a person working as a housewife or mother. It is more common now, too, to observe preferences being expressed by married couples to have smaller families or perhaps to have no children at all. With changing values in society as a whole, different and more accessible or inaccessible alternatives emerge. For example, a single person can now have a family through adoption or foster family opportunities.

To get a better idea about your total life — the things you have done, the values you have held or now hold, and the alternatives you've considered along the way — you might find it useful to look at your life as a "pie" that is divided into a number of pieces. Some of those pieces have already been distributed and sampled, others have yet to be cut. Study the sample of the "pie of life" on the right and then try filling in things you value, things you've done, things you enjoy, and things you expect to do with the rest of your life. The words written around the edge of the pie are meant to suggest some of the things some people experience as they progress through their lives.

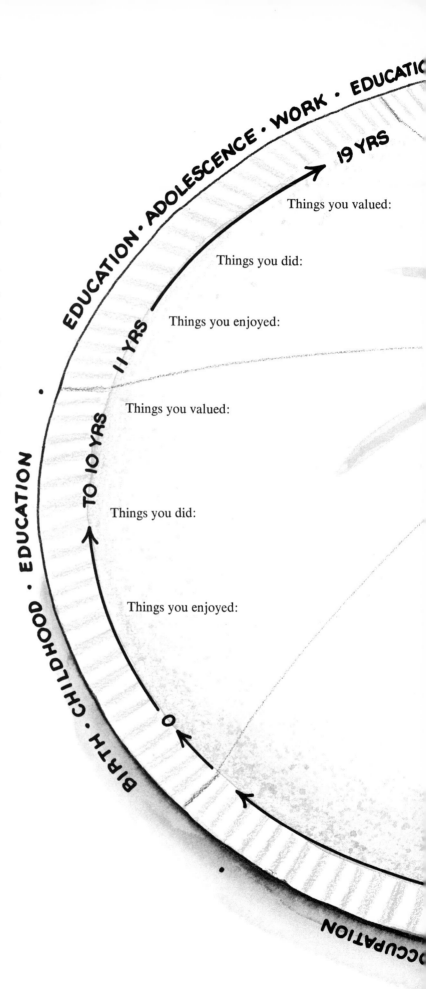

EDUCATION · ADOLESCENCE · WORK · EDUCATIO

19 YRS

Things you valued:

Things you did:

Things you enjoyed:

11 YRS

Things you valued:

TO 10 YRS

Things you did:

Things you enjoyed:

EDUCATION

BIRTH · CHILDHOOD

0

OCCUPATION

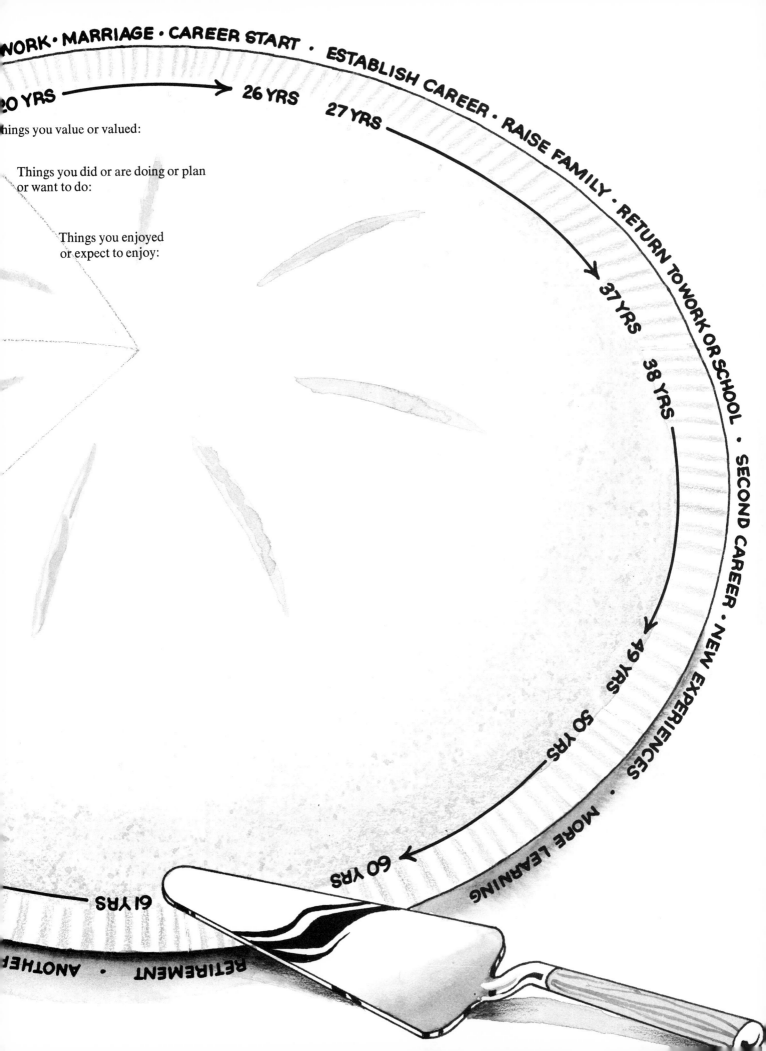

WORK · MARRIAGE · CAREER START · ESTABLISH CAREER · RAISE FAMILY · RETURN TO WORK OR SCHOOL · SECOND CAREER · NEW EXPERIENCES · MORE LEARNING · RETIREMENT · ANOTHER

20 YRS → 26 YRS 27 YRS 37 YRS 38 YRS 49 YRS 50 YRS 60 YRS 61 YRS

Things you value or valued:

Things you did or are doing or plan or want to do:

Things you enjoyed or expect to enjoy:

As you were completing and examining the "pie" of your life, did you discover anything about yourself?_____

_____

_____

_____

Have your values changed over the years?_____

_____

_____

_____

_____

What was the easiest part of the pie to fill in? Why?_____

_____

_____

_____

_____

What are some things that might prove difficult for you in trying to shape and experience the rest of your life the way you want to?_____

_____

_____

_____

_____

How do you expect to divide up your life? In other words, what important activities are you planning for and when?_____

_____

_____

_____

_____

HOW?

It is very difficult, perhaps impossible to formulate what your life might be without knowing what you want . . . and knowing what you want requires that you establish some personal and clear statements of goals for yourself. The exercises in the next pages may help you to begin.

WHEN?

Setting Goals

Some women have expressed discouragement about setting goals because they have set so many they never reached. They see no point in going through the process just to fail again. However, it is important to have goals when you are making life choices for today and tomorrow. They are especially important for giving direction to your energy and for determining how you will spend your time. Setting goals can be a way of getting things moving, and they can be a yardstick against which to measure progress.

WHY?

WHAT?

WHO?

WHERE?

WHETHER?

"If you don't know what you want you probably will never get it."

To be attainable, goals should be realistic and meaningful. They should be based on an understanding of yourself, including your values, interests, strengths, and weaknesses. Goals are statements of the general long-range outcomes you desire. More specific short-range steps toward accomplishment of a goal can be called objectives. If you value being an asset to your community, a goal to which you assign priority might be to make a specific contribution to your community. Specific objectives might be (1) to volunteer to work on at least one civic activity, such as a clean-up campaign; (2) to become a member of one community group and attend all meetings; and (3) to keep up with what's happening in the community.

Describe some aims or goals you have had, indicating whether or not you attained them.

Goal	Attained	Not attained

Consider Susan's case.

When Susan finished high school she wanted only one thing — to get married. Now at age 27, she has a 2½-year-old child and is in the process of getting a divorce from her second husband. She has held several different jobs and has now been working as a veterinarian's assistant for eight months. She has been re-evaluating herself and seeking clarification of her life's purposes. Her values and interests have changed. She feels that she made a serious mistake to reject any thought of college as a part of her future when she was in high school, even deciding not to take the college entrance test. She now considers her personal and educational development to be very important, and she feels a need for achievement. It is important to her that she develop her full potential and make a new, secure life for her child and herself. She wants to become a physician's assistant. However, she must first take the college entrance test and then apply for admission to a training program for physician's assistants.

What are some of Susan's values? _____

_____

_____

_____

What is Susan's primary goal? _____

_____

_____

List some things Susan might do to help attain her goals.

_____

_____

_____

_____

_____

_____

_____

_____

There are two kinds of barriers that often stand in the way of attaining desired goals:

1. *Personal shortcomings* (internal), including such things as aptitudes or abilities, physical strengths, personality, personal attitudes or prejudices, etc.

2. *Obstacles outside of self* (external), including race or sex discrimination, financial needs, educational opportunities, the job market, attitudes of society, family responsibilities, educational background, etc.

What are some other examples of personal shortcomings?_____

_____

_____

_____

What are some other examples of obstacles outside of self?_____

_____

_____

_____

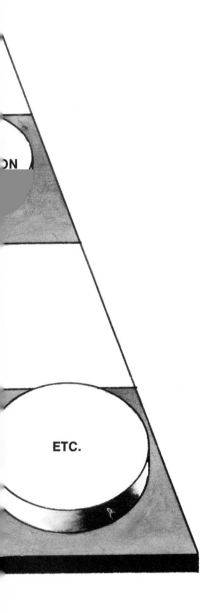

Susan's barriers

List below some personal shortcomings and some obstacles outside herself
that may prevent Susan from reaching her goal.

_____

_____

_____

_____

_____

Action she can take

List steps she could take and/or help she may get from others to remove each
of the barriers listed.

_____

_____

_____

_____

_____

**Re-examine Susan's goal. Is it attainable? What alternative goal(s) might she
consider?**_____

_____

_____

To help you determine meaningful goals for yourself, complete the following:

What you'd like to happen in five years

List here things you would like to learn to do, satisfying activities you'd like to be involved in, and things you want to strive toward during the next five years. Keeping your values in mind, think in terms of occupation, leisure time, family, education, etc.

_____

_____

_____

_____

_____

What you'd like to happen in one year

List here things you would like to learn to do, activities you'd like to be involved in, and things you want to strive toward during the next year. Some of these may be duplications of your first list.

_____

_____

_____

_____

_____

To help you set realistic goals, complete the following:

What you do well (your strengths)

List here the things you do well. Sometimes this is a hard list for women to complete because they have been brought up to be modest, to minimize what they do well in exchange for being popular or for being liked and loved by others.

_____

_____

_____

_____

_____

_____

What you do poorly (your personal shortcomings)

List here the things you do poorly or that cause you concern. Look back at your list of what you would like to happen in five years and see if you can tell whether the things that cause you concern may be obstacles to your attaining those goals.

_____

_____

_____

_____

_____

_____

Now take this information about yourself and convert it into statements of goals that express what you want in life. Select at least one item from your list of what you would like to happen in five years and at least one item from your list of what you would like to happen in one year.

What is your goal?	What are some specific steps (objectives) you can take toward reaching your goal?	When do you want to attain this goal?
_____	_____	
	_____	
	_____	
	_____	_____
_____	_____	
	_____	
	_____	
	_____	
	_____	_____

✓CHECKPOINT

Setting goals and getting ready to move toward what you want

Setting goals for yourself is a way to begin getting some "living space" in your life. To get to a goal, you need to clear a path so that movement toward what you want is possible. Some of the things that have to be cleared from the path are value conflicts, unnecessary or unknown hazards, personal or societal limitations, and various fears or anxieties that often are evident whenever anyone tries to attain something difficult or new.

Just setting goals is one thing, but finding out what you need to know before choosing an action leading to a goal is another matter, which will be considered in the next section.

If you want to begin to move toward what you want, go on to the next section. It's your move.

What do you need to know?

Collecting information and using it in making a decision is probably the most familiar part of the decision-making process for all of us. But in lots of ways it is the most elusive and can cause the most anxieties. First of all, there is no fixed point at which even any one person can say "Now I have enough information." Moreover, if there were such a point it would vary from decision to decision and from individual to individual. One person may decide to take a job when only a brief description of the job and the salary is known. Others would want to know first about the "security" package and the people with whom they'd associate, and others would be able to make a choice only after good information is collected about chances for advancement.

The problem of getting enough information, as well as the best information, is critical in the decision-making process, and it often prevents people from making choices. You probably know people who have faced decisions for years and still have not made them because they say they need more information. In most critical decisions, deciders rarely have all available information in hand before making a choice. In fact, there will generally be a large amount of information that will never be known to them. And information is subject to change. Deciders often grow or change so that the quality and the relevance of information they need fluctuates over even short periods of time.

Mistakes you might be making

There are some common mistakes in gathering and using information that you should know about as you begin to consider the role of information in the decision-making process.

One of the most common is *not choosing to do something because you are not aware that it exists.* Sometimes planning is made difficult because there are so many alternatives available. Some are obvious; some have to be sought out; some probably always remain unknown. Consider, for example, a woman thinking about re-entering college. She does not have the financial resources to pay for four years of education and does not want to go through general education courses to get what she wants—a satisfying job to take up her time when her children grow older. Besides not having the money and not wanting to spend so much time she is afraid she could not pass the entrance test. She chooses to stay home.

What alternatives could there have been? _____

_____

_____

Describe any mistakes you have made because you did not know about certain alternatives. _____

_____

_____

Another common mistake is *choosing to do something even though you do not know what might result*. A student graduating from a large university is notified by her placement office of a job with a large company as a sales trainee. She sends the notice back indicating she will not apply because she knows they would hire a man.

What else could she have done? _____

_____

_____

Little did the student know that the company first asked for names of female applicants only, because it was interested in hiring a woman.

If you can, give an example of a mistake you have made in this category.

_____

_____

Not trying to look ahead to anticipate what might be the results of your choice can prove to be a big mistake since it can prevent you from being prepared for an outcome that was neither anticipated nor desired. Information used correctly can improve your chances of predicting outcomes more accurately.

Underestimating or overestimating the importance of certain information. How many times have you changed your plans or your decisions because of something someone said, especially someone you know or trust? Did you check out their information? A recent TV program featured a woman who refused for years to look for a job because her husband said no one would hire her or pay her to work.

Describe a situation in which you underestimated or overestimated the value of some information. _____

_____

_____

Not knowing what information is most useful and relevant to you in a given decision situation. A college student trying to make a decision about a career finds out which jobs have the highest salaries and makes a choice.

What other information might have been important? _____

_____

_____

How can you make sure you collect useful information?

Although you will rarely feel you have all the information you'd like to have in a critical decision situation, you can do a few things to insure that the information you do get is useful and relevant, as well as reliable:

1. You must know what you want. Clarifying your goals helps you collect information that gets right to the point of the decision.

2. Consider carefully your sources of information. Does the person from whom you're getting your information have any emotional involvement or some stake in telling you only one side of the story?

3. Listen and use information that you didn't want to hear, as well as what you did want or expect to hear. You may get upset by certain information because it is not what you wanted, but in order to make a well-considered choice it's important to process all information that relates to your decision. Try to be aware of when you are being emotional and when you are being objective in your choices.

4. If at all possible, don't rely on one "expert" for your information. Consult several sources with the same information requests. This may be frustrating because you might get quite different information from these sources, but it does help you detect new elements in your choice.

Information Is Power!

Women need power; many haven't had it. Information contributes to how much power an individual has in making a well-informed choice that involves a minimal amount of uncertainty. The fact that sayings about "woman's intuition" are so widely used suggests that women have been stereotyped as tending to use intuitive thought rather than facts or logic in making decisions. This is not to say that intuitive decision-making is always or necessarily wrong. Because women have been taught from birth not to be pushy and not to "make a scene," they may not have developed assertive skills to get information, especially from someone reluctant to give it. Many do not have access to information they need.

Information is power because it helps reduce the uncertainty associated with a critical choice. Suppose there are three available jobs, all of which would give you something you like to do. The only information you have is as follows:

JOB 1

Offers the potential for more than double the pay of the other two jobs. However, there is no security plan—insurance, health benefits, etc.—and most people in this job do not stay with it more than three years, even though they make a lot of money in that time.

JOB 2

Once you are hired in this job you will probably be expected to stay for a long time. Retirement, education, and health benefits are excellent, but the salary is the lowest of any of the three jobs.

What information regarding these three alternatives would help you reduce the uncertainty in your decision? _____

_____

_____

_____

What information gives you the most power? _____

_____

_____

_____

JOB 3

This job has moderate chances for advancement. Most people who work in this job move up a notch or two but rarely reach the higher ranks of the firm. Retirement, health, and education benefits are good, but there is about a 20 percent chance that people who work in this job get laid off permanently within five years.

In a similar situation in real life do you think you could get the information you listed on page 48? How?_____

_____

_____

_____

_____

Sometimes we know what information we want, but a number of things keep us from it. Obstacles, which might be called "gatekeepers," include stereotypes and myths, opinions of others, and pressures exerted by certain cultural attitudes and by our own perceptions of things.

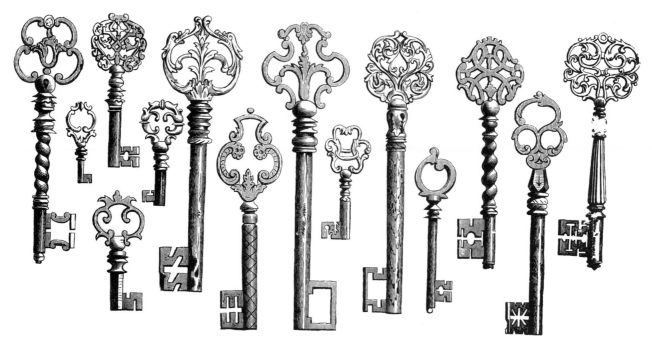

Dealing with gatekeepers: which is myth and which is fact?

Put an "M" next to the items below you consider myth and an "F" next to those you consider fact.

_____ **1.** Women have a poor attendance record at work because of illness.

_____ **2.** At comparable jobs, women have no higher rate of turnover than men.

_____ **3.** A woman must have four years or more of college before she can expect to equal or exceed the pay of a man who dropped out of school after eight years or less.

_____ **4.** Women who work during their lives work for an average of about 12 years.

_____ **5.** Most women who work do so from basic economic necessity.

_____ **6.** Black women have an advantage over black men in finding employment.

_____ **7.** The employment of mothers leads to juvenile delinquency.

See page 53 for the answers.

Sometimes myths are so widespread that they are taken as fact and remain unquestioned. If you had two or more answers incorrect on this exercise, you might find it worth while to evaluate your information more carefully when it comes to making a decision.

Exploding myths that affect your life

Direct your attention now to other outworn myths, held by both men and women, that affect not only the opportunities available to you as a woman but your aspirations and beliefs about yourself as well.

Some women have been prevented from becoming what they could have become because of biases people hold about what females should be and what males should be. Categorize these adjectives according to whether they represent masculine or feminine characteristics. Add others that you can think of to your list.

Characteristics	Feminine	Masculine
Competitive	_____	_____
Independent	_____	_____
Fickle	_____	_____
Active	_____	_____
Sensitive	_____	_____
Gentle	_____	_____
Passive	_____	_____
Ambitious	_____	_____

How do such stereotypes of what is masculine and what is feminine restrict decision-making? _____

_____

Have you been taught by your culture to want certain goals and to restrict yourself to certain behavior? _____

_____

Now look through a magazine and note the advertisements or watch a TV program to see how men and women are depicted. How does a female contestant describe herself—in terms of other people, for example does she say that she is married to a lawyer or that she is the mother of two children? List below other objectives that describe the stereotyped images of men and women in ads.

_____

_____

_____

Why do we hold different images of men and women?_____

_____

_____

Consider some of these statements, which are perceived by some as facts about women.

(1) Women are more verbal; men are more mathematical and scientific.

(2) Women can't really make up their minds; indecision is a typical female trait.

(3) Women are the weaker sex.

(4) There are jobs for men and jobs for women.

What stereotypes, traditions, or myths have affected your life?

_____

_____

_____

Locate at least one fact that proves that the tradition or bias you listed is a myth about women._____

_____

_____

Answers to myths and facts

1. Myth The fact is that the Women's Bureau of the U.S. Department of Labor states (May 1974) that a recent Public Health Service study found that there is less than a fraction of 1 percent difference in the absentee rate of men and women because of illness or injury: 5.6 days a year for women compared with 5.2 for men.

2. Fact At comparable jobs, women have no higher rate of turnover than men. The Women's Bureau of the U.S. Department of Labor states (May 1974) that studies on labor turnover indicate that net differences for men and women are generally small. In one survey by the U.S. Department of Labor (1973) statistics indicate that 11 percent of the men changed jobs one or more times, while only 8.6 percent of the women made such changes.

3. Fact A woman must have four years or more of college before she can expect to equal or exceed the pay of a man who dropped out of school after eight years or less. The *Monthly Labor Review* reports (January 1974) that the median dollar earnings of year-round full-time workers 18 and older, March 1973, were $7,577 for men with eight years or less education and $8,925 for women with four years or more of college. Women with one to three years of college earned $6,465.

4. Myth The fact is that the Women's Bureau reports (May 1974) that the average woman worker has a worklife expectancy of 25 years. Single women average 45 years in the labor force.

5. Fact Most women who work do so from basic economic necessity. The Women's Bureau reports (May 1974) that of the nearly 34 million women in the labor force in March 1973, nearly half were working because of pressing economic need. They were either single, widowed, divorced, or separated or had husbands whose incomes were less than $3,000 a year. Another 4.7 million had husbands with incomes between $3,000 and $7,000—incomes that did not meet criteria established by the Bureau of Labor Statistics for even a low standard of living for an urban family of four. One out of 10 women workers in March 1973 was head of the family.

6. Myth The fact is that unemployment statistics disprove this commonly held belief. The unemployment rates for 1966, 1969, and 1973 were as follows:

	1966	1969	1973*
Black men	6.6%	3.7%	7.6%
Black women	8.8%	6.0%	10.5%

* (Figures for 1973 represent all minority races.)

Unemployment is more severe among black women than among any other group in the population.

7. Myth According to the Women's Bureau (May 1974), studies show that whether or not a mother is employed does not appear to be a determining factor for the causes of juvenile delinquency. Indications are that it is the quality of a mother's care rather than the time consumed in such care that is of major significance.

53

Sometimes others serve as your gatekeepers

When a young woman announced she wanted to go to law school after graduation, a man friend remarked, "You don't want to be like those women."

This kind of statement can prove to be a powerful gatekeeper for people. What do other people think about your goals? In the following exercise, list your goals, and then rank the importance of each goal compared to the others listed—i.e., 1 most important, 2 next most important, etc. Then, next to your own rankings, list how others would want you to rank your goals.

How would others want you to rank your goals?

Your goal	Rank	Friend	Another friend	Parents	Husband

Is there any difference in the rankings? Why? _____

_____

What are some ways you could deal with these differences? _____

_____

_____

Yourself as a gatekeeper

In spite of the many outside forces that have an influence on decision-making, it might be said in general that most people have the freedom to choose when they want to choose. Still, many people do not decide—do not take action—because they don't feel that they are qualified, skilled, or experienced enough. Much of the time this inability to decide stems from being afraid of not succeeding in what they want to do. Consequently, many actions that might be taken are not.

Recently, a woman described herself as her own most difficult gatekeeper. She wanted to return to college after being out of school for 12 years. When she considered enrolling in a college course she was terrified and delayed her decision many times. Among other things, she felt she was not "smart" enough to go to college, that she'd be embarrassed and ignorant among other college students, and that her teachers would make fun of her. After more delay, she did enroll in a community college course tailored for people returning to college. She found she could do the work, and she even enjoyed the experience. For this woman, a poor estimate of her own abilities as well as limited information about alternatives and possible chances for success or failure almost kept her from moving toward an important goal.

What might have resulted if this woman had continued to put off enrolling in a college course?

What are some things that might have happened if she found she couldn't do college work?

What additional alternatives might she be able to pursue if she succeeds with her college career?

If she had failed, would she have been any worse off than she was before trying to do college work?

What important information might be revealed to the woman in this situation?

What are some examples you can recall where you acted as your own gatekeeper?

You can equip yourself to deal more effectively with yourself as a gatekeeper if you try to explore something that appeals to you, even if it seems unrealistic or impossible. Don't undersell yourself! You've accomplished a lot of things that you probably haven't realized or thought about enough.

Consider these statements:

"I got married so I can't."

"I guess we'll stay together for the children."

"I really want to do this, but John has to finish law school first."

"I want it, but nobody else thinks it's a good idea."

"For me, it's simply not a decision! I *have* to raise my children before I can do what I really want to do."

A common means of avoiding responsibility in decision-making is to use these kinds of statements. Sometimes, it is so difficult to consider doing something that you don't realize you have any choice at all. When people say they *have* to do something it really means that they could do other things, but that for one reason or another the thing they have to do has a much higher priority, or it seems to involve more palatable and less threatening consequences for the decider. Remember, to deny self may mean avoiding decisions or responsibility for prior decisions. Avoiding decisions also has consequences.

Sources
of Information

One way to deal with some gatekeepers is to develop good sources of information and new sources of information. You can get some idea about some of the possible sources of information by following Brenda's case, starting on the next page.

Brenda tries to catch up

Brenda has been accepted for admission to "Operation Catch Up," an affirmative action program designed to provide academic, practical, and professional law enforcement training principally for women and members of minority groups. Program participants will receive a $600 stipend each quarter and must agree to employment in the criminal justice field upon completion of the program.

Brenda has already completed two years of study in social work. She thinks being a policewoman will give her an opportunity to have a more interesting kind of life, to gain more insight into what goes into life, to meet different kinds of people, and to do interesting and diversified kinds of things.

The day after Brenda was accepted to the program, her recently widowed mother, who was not well, came to live with her. Brenda panicked. She knew how dependent and demanding her mother could be. Already her mother was complaining about Brenda's not spending enough time with her and about her going into a dangerous field like police work. Brenda now is wondering if she can handle the rigorous training program and academic work and have time to give her mother physical care and the psychological support she needs. Should she drop out of the program and get a job that will be less demanding and more lucrative?

In your opinion, what sources of information are for Brenda the most important? Why do you think some of them are more important than others? Keep these two questions in mind as you complete the following exercise.

Considering Brenda's situation, try to evaluate the things she might think about and the sources of information listed below. Put a (VI) next to Very Important sources of information, an (I) next to those that are Important, and an (NI) next to those that are Not Important.

Things to think about

Alternative career fields _____

The attitude of society toward women in law enforcement _____

What her work values are _____

What life style she desires in the future _____

What activities she really enjoys _____

What her immediate objectives are _____

What she wants in the future _____

What outcome she can expect if she gets this training _____

What other people she cares for want her to do _____

What her responsibilities are toward her mother _____

Her mother _____

Other family members _____

The director of the program _____

The financial aid director at the school _____

Things to read

Occupational information in the social services area _____

Information on job market now and in the future _____

Information on women in the field _____

Things to do

Consider hiring someone to care for her mother _____

Look into other sources of care for her mother _____

Talk to people in law enforcement about women
    in the field _____

Assess the risks in law enforcement _____

Assess her financial situation _____

Explore other alternatives _____

What other sources might you suggest that Brenda consider? _____

_____

_____

_____

_____

_____

_____

Your Own Case Study

Write a description of a personal decision that you are facing, one that you feel is an important choice for you at the present time. List the sources of information that have helped you or could help you with that decision. ____

_____

_____

_____

_____

_____

What other sources would you like to be able to consult? (You might refer to the list used for Brenda's case.) _____

_____

_____

_____

_____

✔ # CHECKPOINT

Gathering and Evaluating Information

Can you think of other mistakes you have made when you were gathering information before making a decision?

1. _____

_____

2. _____

_____

3. _____

_____

4. _____

_____

Experience and information

These pictures with their accompanying questions and instructions offer a framework for reacting and relating to certain settings and experiences. The way you interpret them reflects your experiences of the past, which could affect how you view things that happen to you in the future. What do your past experiences tell you about these pictures?

Describe what is taking place in this picture. What is the relationship of the woman to the man? What is each one doing? Describe the man's feelings toward the woman. Are there things you would like to change in this picture?

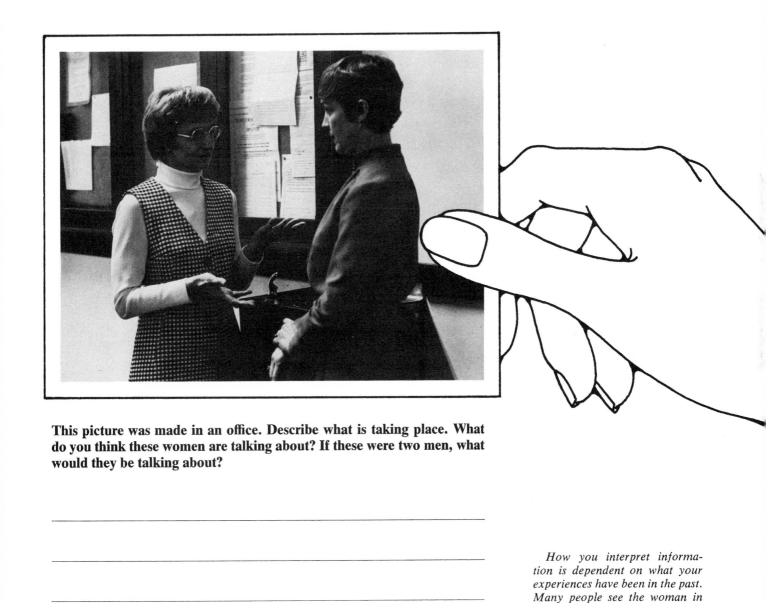

This picture was made in an office. Describe what is taking place. What do you think these women are talking about? If these were two men, what would they be talking about?

How you interpret information is dependent on what your experiences have been in the past. Many people see the woman in the first picture as the secretary to the man. Actually the woman is dean of student affairs and the man is dean of the college at a small liberal arts college. In the second picture, women are often seen as talking about hair styles, what they plan for dinner, etc. Two men would be seen as discussing politics, business matters, etc. What do you think?

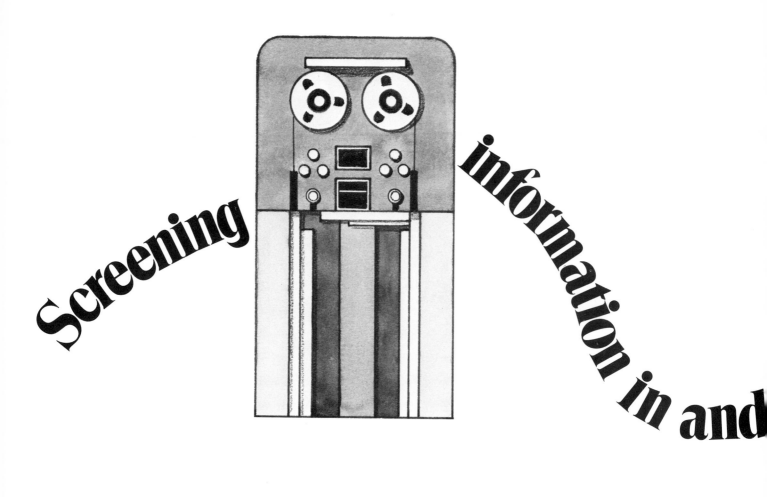

Screening information in and

The way we interpret things, then, the way we "screen" things through our emotions or preconceived expectations, and at times through our resistance to truth, has some impact on the decisions we make. So emotion plays a role in the type and quality of information we collect, and so does *experience*. Often in our search for information we tend to stop searching immediately when a friend or a person we respect for having certain knowledge says that something is so. Regardless of how experienced or expert a person might be, he or she is subject to the same information mistakes or shortcomings that all of us are. It is important to question the source and accuracy of information. You might ask your friends or "experts" how certain they are that what they have told you is true. What was their source of information? Or it may be a case when more than one source of information might have to be investigated, such as when one has a medical or legal problem and consults several doctors or lawyers before coming to a decision.

It is difficult to determine accurately how much information we screen. For example, emotions and poor listening skills can affect how we respond to what others have to say.

A useful, quick check can be made with a friend. You might select a topic about which you have some difference of opinion and talk to each other about it, trying to convince the other person of the correctness of your point of view. Do this for about five minutes and then try to tell your friend what he or she said. See how accurate you are. Where do you spot inaccuracies? Was it a case of simply missing a point, or was it that you didn't want to hear it? The same exercise can be done by taping a political speech or an advertisement on radio or TV and trying to explain what you heard before you play the tape back.

Screening **information out**

What's Your Best Source of Information?

Try to think of a place away from home where you'd like to spend the next year of your life. Don't worry about cost or any kind of family obligations; they will be provided for in some acceptable fashion. Just try to decide where you will spend 365 days. Complete the following:

1. What places (alternatives) can you immediately think of where you'd like to spend 365 days? List them:

_____

_____

_____

_____

2. How much do you know about each of these alternatives? Rate each one: know a lot about it; know a little about it; know nothing concrete about it; would just like to go there.

_____

_____

_____

_____

3. Now try to classify your sources of information relating to each of the alternatives. Classify the information: (E) experience, if you've been there; (H) heard about it from reliable people whose judgment you respect; (R) read about it in some detail; (F) know little about it but just feel you'd like to go there. Each alternative you list may have more than one—or none—of the categories.

Alternative	Type of Information
_____	_____
_____	_____
_____	_____
_____	_____
_____	_____

4. What response appeared most frequently?

_____

_____

_____

How certain are you about the validity of the information you have?

_____

_____

5. If you did have to choose a place to go, what additional information do you think you'd need? Why?

_____

_____

_____

What source(s) would you explore to get this information?

_____

_____

_____

Developing alternatives

Searching for information helps ultimately in the choice among alternatives, but it also helps in finding new alternatives and different combinations of alternatives that might prove to be the best action to take in a given situation.

If we are making well-considered decisions we are constantly trying to learn about new alternatives. But we may never know all the alternatives in a given situation, and we generally have to make a choice without knowing. Try to keep this in mind when you complete the exercises in the next four pages.

In the past, many women have had only a few alternatives for how to spend their entire lives. Social changes have created new alternatives for men and women. A simple way to help you know about the alternatives at a decision point is to follow the five steps below.

Step 5

*Begin predicting
what might result if
you choose each of
the alternatives.*

Step 4

*After consulting
these sources, add
the new alternatives
to those you have
already identified.*

Step 3

*List the sources of
help in discovering
new alternatives.*

Step 2

*Write down the
existing alternatives
you know about
now.*

Step 1

*Define the decision,
including when it
has to be made.*

Alternatives

Janice is single, black, and 26 years of age. She has a four-year degree in business education and a master's degree in counseling. At present Janice is working as an affirmative action counselor at a large university. She enjoys her work very much, is quite anxious to enhance her professional skills, and is thinking seriously of returning to school in pursuit of a Ph.D. degree in counselor education at a university noted throughout the country for its outstanding counseling department. Janice is very lonely, and she has made few friends. She does not believe in interracial dating or marriage, but she would like very much to date and someday marry a man who is at least her equal or her superior. At her institution, there are only a few black men on the campus, and most of them are married. Although Janice desires to enhance her professional skills, she fears that the pursuit of a Ph.D. degree will virtually eliminate her chances of finding a mate.

and life styles

List the alternatives you see for Janice. What are the advantages and disadvantages of each alternative? How would her life style be affected by each?

Alternative	Advantages	Disadvantages	Possible outcomes

What alternative do you think is best for Janice? Why? _____

_____

What sources could she consult to help develop more alternatives? _____

_____

Are there any new alternatives?

The case of Dinah is another situation that requires examining alternatives, and perhaps even developing new ones.

Dinah is completing her junior year of college. She has gone through her college years mainly on loans and scholarships. At present, she will owe about $8,000 after completing her four years of college.

Dinah is totally self-supported. She is from a very poor family and has no financial resources available from them. She needs about $500 to complete her junior year, but she has exhausted all state and federal sources and cannot borrow from a bank. She is exploring some private foundations for the money.

Dinah could work several days a week, but she worked during her sophomore year and fell behind in her courses. She had to take incompletes, which she must make up by the end of her junior year. All her grades have been at least Bs, and most have been As. She has been told that she can go on welfare, but she has strong personal reasons for not doing this. Now Dinah is desperate: she cannot pay her basic bills (gas and electric) and is a month behind on her rent ($125 per month). If she doesn't pay these bills in 30 days she will be evicted.

What action(s) can Dinah take?

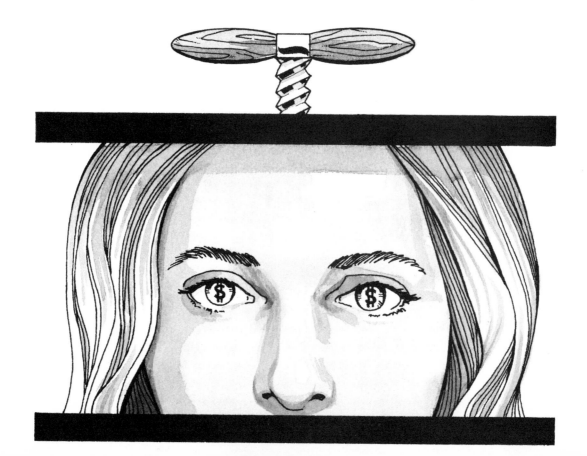

What are some possible obstacles and outcomes (results) for each of the actions she might take?

Action	Obstacles	Possible outcomes

What additional information would you want in order to help Dinah?

_____

What alternative would you recommend? _____

What is the risk involved? _____

Dinah decided that she would continue at all costs. She gave up her apartment and shared one with a friend. She took a job one day a week and applied for a special foundation scholarship, which she received after waiting six months.

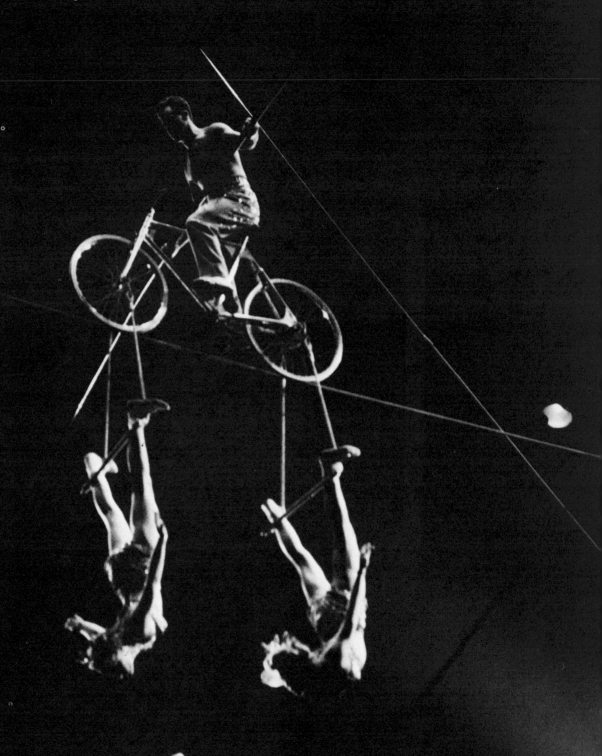

Your risk-taking behavior

Choosing an available action is difficult. It requires that one consider the risk involved and also the desirability of an outcome that one expects to result from an action that is taken.

The combination of risk and desirability that you attach to each outcome is the plan or strategy you use in making a decision. Risk-taking may vary from decision to decision, or it may be fairly consistent over several different critical choices. Different people may risk more for something that is especially desirable.

The following exercises are geared to help you develop a plan for taking action and making a choice.

When you think about some of the important decisions you've made, how do you rate as a risk taker?

Important decisions	**Risk involved**
_____	_____
_____	_____
_____	_____
_____	_____

Were there differences in the risks involved? Why? _____

_____

_____

How do you rate yourself as a risk taker? (very safe, usually on the safe side, on the risky side, often choose a very high risk action) _____

_____

Now try to think about all the decisions you have made. What is the biggest risk you've ever taken? _____

_____

_____

How do you know it was the biggest risk? _____

_____

_____

Why did you take this risk? _____

How did it turn out? Describe. _____

_____

_____

_____

Risk-taking

The following exercises show you how to consider risk in formulating a plan or strategy for taking action.

The arithmetic of supply and demand indicates that the traditional fields of employment for women will not be able to absorb the tremendous increase in the number of women college graduates expected in the 1970-80 period. Unless a much larger proportion of women enter other, high-demand professions, the outlook for college-educated women may be less favorable than it has been in recent years.

Only 12.2% of physicians are women
*Only 4.9% of lawyers and judges are women
*Only 3.5% of dentists are women
*Only 1.6% of engineers are women
*Only 3.6% of architects are women
*Only 12.0% of pharmacists are women

Only 21.1% of college and university teachers are women
*Only 13.7% of life and physical scientists are women
Only 19.4% of bank officials and financial managers are women

If you find yourself putting off the task of making a decision to prepare for an occupation, especially one in which men are dominant, it most likely is because you want to be certain you are making the wisest decision. You may say to yourself something like "I'd like to do different things — but only if I could do so without any long-term commitment, work, or risks."

Try finishing the following story:

An interest test Jane takes indicates that her interests are in mechanical, scientific, and computational areas. Satisfying occupations for people with those interests are engineering, physics, etc. Jane's counselor cautions her to be "realistic" about her decision._____

_____

_____

_____

_____

_____

_____

*Department of Commerce, Bureau of the Census, 1970 Annual Averages. Other statistics are from U.S. Department of Labor, Employment Standard Administration, Women's Bureau, Washington, D.C. 20210.

What does the way you completed this story reveal about how much risk you are willing to take?

_____

_____

_____

It is advantageous to identify the alternatives and to weigh the advantages and disadvantages of choosing a field that relatively few women go into. What are the advantages of such professions for women? _____

_____

_____

_____

What would be a "realistic" decision for you if you were in Jane's situation?

_____

_____

Sometimes we perceive risk as a kind of barrier preventing us from getting to what we want. But understanding the degree of uncertainty involved in a choice can help in the development of alternative choices. When we encounter a real barrier, we generally decide how to deal with it in terms of what it is preventing us from achieving. For example, you may not feel that a college degree is worth having if it requires spending a great deal of time studying. Once you decide not to deal with this barrier, you can forget about achieving your goal (a college degree), or you can develop other alternatives for achieving your goal — you could go to an easier college, you could cheat, or you could spend a longer period of time before you have enough credits to get a degree.

Some common barriers are listed below. Try to think of a specific educational or career goal that you have ("I want to be a lawyer"), and then rate each of the common barriers in terms of whether it would be worth the risk to deal with this barrier. Rate the barriers either 1 for worth the risk or 2 for not worth the risk, according to the degree of risk you see related to each barrier.

Goal: _____

Barrier	*Rating*
1. Being thought you are more masculine than feminine	_____
2. Not getting admitted to a medical, law, or appropriate school	_____
3. "Wasting" the cost of your education	_____
4. Handling the course work in college	_____
5. The length of training	_____
6. Fear of not getting married	_____
7. Facing job-hunting restrictions	_____
8. Facing attitudes of professors	_____
9. Being in an unknown environment	_____
10. Competing successfully with males	_____

Now, in each case what are some possible results of either dealing with the barrier or not bothering to deal with it?

Barrier and your rating	*Possible results of deciding or not deciding to take the risk*
_____	_____
_____	_____
_____	_____
_____	_____
_____	_____
_____	_____
_____	_____
_____	_____

How to deal with uncertainty in developing a plan for action

A plan for action involves putting together all the elements of the decision-making process. Since all important decisions probably involve some risk or uncertainty, how you will finally choose will depend on how you will handle the uncertainty of that decision. When a person decides what plan will be used in a decision, it is generally a choice between *how likely it is that an outcome will occur* and *how desirable the outcome is*. Sometimes you may pick something that is highly desirable but has little chance of being successful or of happening at all. For example, if a woman decides not to finish school because she wants marriage and a family only, she should be aware that statistics, such as the rising divorce rate and the fact that by the time she is 30 or 35 her last child is in school, make the expected outcomes from that plan highly unlikely. In any case, your plan for action is what ultimately helps you make a choice or take action, and it requires that you weigh how much chance something has of happening along with its desirability.

The following exercise relating to Greta's decision is an introduction to understanding how you can build a plan for action in your life.

Greta has a liberal arts degree from a major university. She married after she graduated and went to Miami with her husband, who joined a law firm. He hopes to set up his own law practice some day. Greta started to work with an insurance company and enjoyed it tremendously. She stopped to have one child and then returned to work toward becoming a sales manager because she liked a challenge and felt she could motivate and encourage others if she were in a managerial job. Her supervisor helped her plan a program to move toward that goal. As she approached the day she could assume such a position, it became apparent that there was no opening of this kind in her office. Now she has been offered a job as a sales manager in another city. She wonders if her husband might be willing to leave his law firm. She wonders if the added responsibility will interfere with her family responsibilities.

How does Greta decide what to do?

Greta's values are: _____

_____

_____

Greta's alternatives are: _____

_____

_____

Additional information Greta needs: _____

_____

_____

Greta's risk-taking profile: Some plans for deciding

Assume that Greta's family is more important to her than anything else in her life. Given that assumption, what action would she take if she chooses to ignore any risk and do what she wants to do? Her plan could lead to her most desired result — a happy family.

_____

_____

_____

Now assume that Greta's career is most important. What would she do in that case if she decides to ignore any risk and does what she wants to do? Her plan could lead her to her most desired result — a successful career.

_____

_____

_____

If she values her family the most, what would Greta do if she decides on the plan that has the best chance of happening, a plan that will most likely be successful? If she values her career the most?

_____

_____

_____

If a combination of career and marriage are important to Greta, what would she do if she decides to pursue a plan that will bring her a combination of what is possible and desirable to her?

_____

_____

_____

Common ways of dealing with uncertainty, then, are:

1. Choosing the alternative that could lead to the most desired result, regardless of risk

2. Choosing the alternative that is most likely to be successful or has the highest probability of happening

3. Choosing the alternative that has both high probability and high desirability

There are other ways of dealing with uncertainty — impulsively choosing the first alternative you know of, letting someone else decide for you, or postponing any action until a later time.

What plan of action would you take? Why? _____

_____

_____

Now consider, in terms of the risk involved, a recent decision you've made or a decision you're about to make. What plans for action did you consider or are you considering?

The critical decision: _____

Alternative action	Predictable outcome	Desirability of the outcome?	Possibility of the outcome?	Risk involved?
_____	_____	_____	_____	_____
_____	_____	_____	_____	_____
_____	_____	_____	_____	_____

What did you or will you decide? _____

_____

What type of plan or strategy have you employed or will you employ? (i.e., high risk, high desirability, etc.) _____

_____

✓ **CHECKPOINT**

What is your favorite or most frequently applied risk-taking plan?

_____

What does your selection of this plan tell you about yourself?

_____

Has your plan been effective in reaching your goals? Explain.

_____

_____

The remaining part of this book deals with taking action. If you want to see how you might begin to move toward what you want in life, go on to the next page. It's your life!

HOW

do you take action?

I want to take action, but…

"What my mother is hoping is that Prince Charming will come along and take me away."

"Everybody seems to know what I ought to do except me."

"I can't make up my mind."

"When I do decide, I can't seem to stick with my choice."

Part of being able to take action—to make a decision—requires being able to respond to the kinds of situations that action may present. It might mean having to deal with a new life style, with some initial adjustments in personal relationships, or it might mean just learning to deal with the day-to-day problems of living in a male-dominated world.

Many adjustments that are likely to be required can be predicted, others cannot. So it is important to add some resources to your abilities and skills that will help you deal

effectively with the many day-to-day decisions you will have to face.

One way you may help yourself deal with the variety of situations encountered in your new or changing role is to learn how to respond assertively, with an appropriate expression of your feelings, beliefs, and opinions. Assertive behavior is not a cure-all for dealing with people, nor is it always the best approach to use when dealing with all people. Rather, it is a way of communicating effectively without putting down yourself or somebody else.

The profiles described on the next page probably resulted, at least in part, from the ability of these women to express what is important to them to the important people in their lives. From this initial step of asserting what they want they have developed a variety of alternatives and have pursued or have begun to pursue them.

Seven women who did

"Selmaree Oster lives in Greenwich Village and is a research biologist at Mount Sinai Hospital, where she assists her husband, Gerald, a professor of biophysics. As a wife and as stepmother/friend to Gerald's two children, she runs her home life with the same authority and spirit she brings to her life as a scientist."

"Louise Feinsot thrives on working at two jobs (both paid), running her household and sharing her life with her husband and three children. Not bad for someone who, just a few years ago, was fretting at the restrictions of housekeeping and motherhood. Today, necessity rules and everyone pitches in to help."

"Elizabeth Browning Karpf, recently divorced after 18 years of marriage, has changed her life style from full-time suburban wife and mother to full-time suburban career woman and part-time mother of four. Her life demands lots of energy and split-second timing. She starts her days at dawn and by eight o'clock in the morning has the household organized and ready to go."

"Mildred Johnstone, at 75, is the same free spirit she was at 25. Her life style, the study of philosophy, Eastern religions, and people, is her art. The core of Millie's life these days is the Japanese tea ceremony."

"Susanna D'Alton and Mary O'Neill have been friends since their high school days in New York. Now they share a railroad flat and are exploring the world of careers. Susie works for the American Federation of the Arts, is a volunteer at New York Hospital, and dabbles in crafts. Mary teaches 4-year-olds in a Montessori school and hopes to enter law school."

"Anahid Ajemian Avakian is a concert violinist, wife, and mother of three. She'd like to make her living playing quartets, but she is not above fiddling backgrounds for commercials. Anahid, highly organized, bemoans the fact that she can't organize the rest of the family to her high standards."

Role models

Reflecting on women and men you have known, describe below the characteristics of some who may have been models you attempted to follow in your own life. Indicate the areas of their lives, including qualities they possess, that have particularly influenced your life. You may have to think carefully because some of them may have affected your life indirectly.

_____

_____

_____

_____

_____

_____

_____

_____

Although the seven women described on page 80, and probably also your role models, have taken some action, they have not necessarily found the answer to their lives as they relate to work, education, or personal relationships. These women have begun to search for those combinations of things in their lives that will bring them closer to outcomes they consider satisfactory and satisfying. Searching and bringing control to your life so that you have a better chance to get what you want is no easy task. You know from reading previous pages that it requires a thorough investigation of yourself, your values, and goals. It also requires a search for appropriate options and information that will help you decide among those options, and at the same time enable you to make better predictions of the outcomes that might follow the action you take.

Behaving assertively can be of help to you throughout the decision-making process, and some useful guidelines to assertive behavior are described and demonstrated on the following pages.

What are your rights as a decider?

In a society described as free, the right to choose is assumed to exist for all individuals. Certain rights are guaranteed people through a variety of laws, both written and unwritten, and through a complex network of societal values, attitudes, and beliefs that may be quite visible or somewhat elusive, depending on the person and the dynamics of a given decision-making situation. It is important that you be aware of these rights and learn to deal with any limitations that might exist for you because you do not exercise them.

If you are not confident about your skills as a decision-maker, the tendency is to opt out of choices and, consequently, to avoid taking specific action. This means that others will tend to make the decisions that will affect your life. If you do let others make your decisions, you are still the one who is responsible for those choices, and it is you who must live with them until you do take action.

Consider your rights in the following example.

You want to go back to school, but you have two children of preschool age.

What are your rights? What action could you take? You have a right to go back to school. There is no formal law that says you can't go back. There is, however, considerable pressure from people in our society who might discourage you from going back. For example, your mother or husband might say, "A mother shouldn't go back to school or work until her children have completed school." Many women feel they have no choice because there is so much societal pressure on them to raise their children before they do anything else on a full-time basis. The fact remains that the person in this situation does have a choice. Some alternatives would be (1) to go to school full time; (2) to go part time and send the children to a day-care center or find other care for them while she's at school; (3) to wait until the children have completed secondary school; (4) to go back to school once her children begin school and hire somebody to look after them after school hours until she comes home.

All these alternatives have been chosen by some women, and each might be the "best" for a specific person. The point is that a choice does exist, and each has its advantages and disadvantages as far as the individual decider is concerned.

Study the following examples and try to assess each according to what rights you might have as a decision-maker.

What's legal?

You apply for an executive training program in retail sales. You are accepted, but the salary offered you is less than that of a comparable trainee who is a man. **What are your rights?**

What action would you take?_____

_____

_____

_____

_____

In the above case you have some legal rights, and you would be well advised to get legal counsel regarding this situation. You might choose to take other actions as well.

What's normal?

As a single person you wish to pursue a business career. Many of your relatives and married friends say you ought to be settling down and leading a more "normal" existence. What are your rights in this situation? What are some consequences that might occur if you choose to pursue the life you want and not what others recommend for you?

In this decision situation, the pressures from others are quite difficult and at times painful. Many people value the opinions of others. But when you let the opinions of others be the deciding factor you should realize that you are then saying that their opinions are more important than anything else you value.

Many people never get a chance to take action in their lives because they are fearful of going against what others advise, or they are reluctant to stand up for a value that is important to them personally. Knowing and believing in your interpersonal rights is crucial in being able to deal with critical decisions, especially when they involve a consideration of others or what others believe is best for you.

Understanding and accepting certain basic interpersonal rights is an important principle of assertive behavior. Most interpersonal rights are so simple and so much a part of everyday experience that many people are not even aware that they are using them. Many people who tend not to stand up for themselves and their rights apparently do not consider that they have a right to their feelings, beliefs, and opinions. Consider the following "legitimate interpersonal rights."

- The right to say no without feeling guilty.
- The right to decide how to use your own time.
- The right to have feelings, even angry or illogical feelings.
- The right to ask others to change their behavior if it affects you in some concrete way.
- The right to have an opinion different from others and to express it.
- The right to make some mistakes along the way.

How would you handle the following situation in terms of your interpersonal rights?

Laura and her husband were planning a long-awaited vacation trip. Less than a week before they were to leave, Laura's friend Julia came to ask a big favor of her. Julia wanted to go with her husband to a convention, and she wanted Laura to keep their 2½-year-old daughter for the four days they would be away. Julia knew that Laura had lots to do to get ready for the trip she and her husband were taking, but Julia said that she could not go with her husband to the convention unless she could make satisfactory arrangements for her little girl. She said "I know I shouldn't ask, but we really want to go on this convention, and you know I'd do the same for you." Laura felt guilty because she really did not want to keep the child, but she felt that she could not refuse her friend's request. Laura kept the child, and as a result she and her husband had to delay their trip for one day.

What interpersonal rights are involved?_____

_____

_____

_____

How did Laura feel toward Julia for making this request?_____

_____

_____

How might Laura have felt toward herself for being nonassertive and violating her own right to refuse Julia's request?_____

_____

_____

Write a response Laura might have made that would have supported her own rights._____

_____

_____

_____

Assertiveness as a strategy

Assertive behavior is important in many career-related situations. For example, you need to be assertive when you are talking about your educational or career decisions with significant others (husband, close friends, parents). Appropriate assertive behavior can bring about good results for you, for example in job interviews or in dealing with other people in a job.

Basic to developing assertive skills is the ability to distinguish among nonassertive, assertive, and aggressive behaviors:

Nonassertive.

Many women may be characterized as nonassertive. They have been carefully conditioned to be self-denying and submissive, not to stand up for themselves, and to allow their personal rights to be violated by others. Their behavior communicates "I'm not okay; you're okay." "I'm weak; you're strong."

Assertive.

The assertive woman believes in the basic human rights of all persons. She stands up for herself, expressing her feelings honestly and comfortably while respecting the other person's rights. Her goal is for fair play and two-way communication. Her attitude is "I'm okay and so are you."

Aggressive.

The aggressive woman stands up for herself and her rights, but in such a way that the rights of the other person are violated. Her goal is to dominate, to get her own point across. Communication is one way, and the message is "I count; you don't."

The following examples represent four typical situations that call for assertive behavior and often cause difficulty for nonassertive or aggressive people. Each situation is presented with alternative responses that may be characterized as assertive, nonassertive, or aggressive.

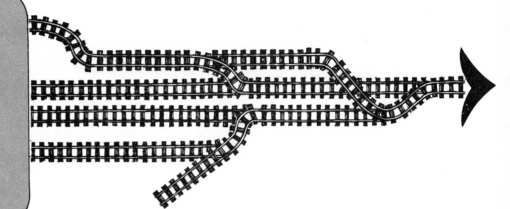

Presenting ideas articulately

Presenting ideas articulately is basic to effective communication and is an important component of assertive responses.

It's 10 o'clock at night, and your family knows you are going to start your new job tomorrow. Your husband and sons bring you their dirty baseball uniforms and tell you that they have to have them by 4 o'clock the next day.

What human rights would you have in this situation?

_____

_____

Why is an assertive response difficult? _____

_____

_____

Your response is:

1. I'm going to bed. Do your own washing.
2. Hand them to me. You know I'll do them.
3. I can see that you need to get these uniforms washed tonight, but I start my new job tomorrow morning and I really should go to bed. Please take care of it yourself.

Which of the above responses is:

1. Nonassertive?_____

Why?_____

_____

2. Aggressive?_____

Why?_____

_____

3. Assertive?_____

Why?_____

_____

Responding to condescending remarks

Women must be prepared to respond to condescending remarks when they enter male-dominated professions or move up the career ladder.

You have approached your employer with a constructive suggestion for organizing the work procedure in the office. He says that he thinks this is a good idea and that he will ask one of the men staff members to implement the change.

What human rights would you have in this situation? _____

_____

Why is an assertive response difficult? _____

_____

Your response is:

1. All right. I'm glad you like the idea.
2. You men think only men can handle responsibility. This was my suggestion, and I'll not stand for some man getting all the credit for it.
3. I think that I can make the change without any difficulty. Do you mind if I handle it?

Which of the above responses is:

1. Nonassertive? _____ **Why?** _____
2. Aggressive? _____ **Why?** _____
3. Assertive? _____ **Why?** _____

Giving negative feedback

It is especially difficult for women with supervisory responsibilities to correct employees' inappropriate behavior. Women have been brought up to seek approval from others.

Two clerical workers in your office have been taking long coffee breaks. The work has been piling up. Others have been complaining about their being away from their desks so long. You are their supervisor.

What human rights would you have in this situation? _____

_____

Why is an assertive response difficult? _____

_____

Your response is:

1. You say nothing to the employees but mumble to others about the way work is piling up.
2. You go into the office room where others are sitting around and say in a loud voice, "Get back to your desks. You have abused your coffee privilege for the last time. I have a good mind to fire you right now."
3. When they return to their desks, you say, "I know how easy it is for time to slip by when you are relaxing and talking to your friends during coffee break. But your work is piling up, and I would like you to stay within the 20-minute break."

Which of the above responses is:

1. Nonassertive? _____ **Why?** _____
2. Aggressive? _____ **Why?** _____
3. Assertive? _____ **Why?** _____

Presenting ideas persuasively

In working with individuals or groups, it is important that your thoughts be clearly stated and that your points of view are brought out effectively.

You are being interviewed for a job as a sales representative. The interviewer asks you what makes you think you can handle a sales job.

What human rights would you have in this situation?_____

_____

Why is an assertive response difficult?_____

_____

Your response is:

1. Well, I can try. I just need to get out of the house and away from the children.
2. I don't know why you should question me, a woman 10 years older than you, about what I can do. I could do your job in a snap. You only have it because you're a man.
3. With four children, persuasion is necessary to get things done. Many times I have had to "sell" a child on wearing certain clothes or studying. I know many women in the community who respect my opinions and will listen to what I have to say about your product.

Which of the above responses is:

1. Nonassertive?_____**Why?**_____
2. Aggressive? _____**Why?**_____
3. Assertive? _____**Why?**_____

 **CHECKPOINT**

Think of a situation you have recently faced that required an assertive response:_____

_____

What human rights were involved?_____

_____

What would have been a nonassertive response?_____

_____

An aggressive response?_____

_____

An assertive response?_____

_____

Components of Assertive Behavior

Many women find that knowing how to express themselves verbally in an assertive manner is only part of learning how to be assertive. Some other necessary considerations are nonverbal and may be tied in with body language. The body does communicate, and being aware of some of the basic components of assertive behavior can make one aware of the body messages being conveyed. Eye contact, facial expressions, body posture, gestures, voice tone and volume, and style of dress are discussed and explained by Alberti and Emmons and by Phelps and Austin (see complete references to their work at the end of this book).

Dealing with emotions

Sometimes you may have difficulty making the kind of measured, thoughtful response you'd like to make. You might be upset or angry, and an assertive response may be too difficult or even seem inappropriate to you.

There are ways to handle your emotions assertively so that you can communicate what's important to you without turning your listener off. The guidelines below are worth considering.

It's all right to be angry

Check the categories below that indicate how you usually handle your anger:

_____ Lose your "cool" and lash out at the other person
_____ Withdraw
_____ Say nothing
_____ Cry
_____ Overapologize, feel inadequate, say "I'm sorry"

_____ Say something humorous but continue to burn inside
_____ Go blank
_____ Talk, talk, talk but say nothing
_____ Stand up for yourself without putting anyone else down

An aggressive outburst is frequently an over-reaction to past pent-up anger. Letting someone know your angry feelings at the time they occur can be assertive.

Study the angry exchanges in the "conversion table" below.

CONVERSION TABLE

Aggressive	Assertive
Husband: Why don't you keep this house cleaner?	**Husband:** Why don't you keep this house cleaner?
Wife: What do you mean? You live here, too!	**Wife:** I like a clean house, too, but with my job I don't have time to get everything done. I'd like you to share some of the responsibility and help keep the house clean.
Husband: I work all day and don't get home until six. You get home at four.	**Husband:** Well, I don't get home until six. You get home at four. That should give you plenty of time.
Wife: You have the sensitivity of an ox. You know how tired I am when I get home. You think there's no work in teaching.	**Wife:** I am very tired when I get home from school and I often still have papers to grade. I feel angry when I see you refusing to help me when I am so tired and feel under pressure with so much to do. I'd like you to help me keep the house clean.
Can you guess how this argument will end?	**Husband:** Well, maybe I haven't realized how much you have to do.
	How is this argument different?
_____	_____
_____	_____
_____	_____
_____	_____

To handle anger assertively, follow these guidelines:

Use "I" messages. Say "I feel really angry when you do things like that" not "you are so stupid for doing that." No one likes to feel that he or she doesn't count for much as a person, so making others responsible for your anger or downgrading them because you feel angry only intensifies the problem. In other words, own your own feelings.

Try to be sure that your statements are nonevaluative. Say "I'd prefer it if you would . . ." not "You are awful because you . . ."

Acknowledge that you hear the other person (instead of listening only to your angry feelings).

Sometimes it may not be enough to ask another person for something. You may have to point out specific behaviors that are different from what was promised or expected. Say "As I recall, you were going to . . . but you haven't. Has something happened?"

Make your own conversion table below by writing a sketch on the left side setting up a situation during which you become angry. On the right side practice responding to the situation until you feel you know how you could handle your anger assertively.

Your Sketch	Assertive Response

Learning to behave assertively will be of some help to you when you are going through the critical stage of taking action, of moving closer to what you want. It will also help you cope with and be responsible for your choice when you're challenged by other people whose opinions you may value or whose behavior may have some impact on your life, your work, or your personal relationships. The following pages in this book are designed to help you develop a plan for actually taking action.

 **CHECKPOINT**

Indicate which of these things might hinder your taking action and in what way.

☐ Anxiety _____

☐ Family responsibility or considerations _____

_____

☐ Consequences _____

☐ Lack of understanding on the part of others

_____

☐ Emotions blocking reality _____

☐ Insecurity _____

☐ Unselfishness _____

☐ Fear _____

☐ Fear of deciding _____

☐ Laziness or inertia _____

☐ Wavering _____

☐ Dependence on others _____

☐ Lack of confidence _____

☐ Failure to stick with choice to see if it works

_____

☐ Guilt _____

☐ Uncertainty _____

☐ Being overwhelmed _____

☐ Responsibility vs. desire vs. capabilities _____

_____

☐ Lack of long-range objectives _____

☐ Finances _____

☐ Fear of failure _____

☐ Need to succeed _____

☐ Ambivalence _____

☐ Frustration _____

☐ Time _____

What are some other things that keep you from taking action?

_____

_____

_____

_____

Before taking action
take another look at your role as a woman

"They emancipate women in universities and in law courts, but continue to regard her as an object of enjoyment. Teach her, as she is taught among us, to regard herself as such, and she will always remain an inferior being. Either with the help of those scoundrels the doctors she will prevent the conception of offspring—that is, will be a complete prostitute, lowering herself not to the level of an animal but to the level of a thing—or she will be what the majority of women are, mentally diseased, hysterical, unhappy, and lacking capacity for spiritual development. High schools and universities cannot alter that. It can only be changed by a change in men's outlook on women and women's way of regarding themselves."

TOLSTOY, *THE KREUTZER SONATA*

What are some things you could do to change men's outlook on women?

_____

_____

_____

To alter women's ways of regarding themselves?_____

_____

_____

_____

Are any of the actions you've described above important to you? Why?

_____

_____

Are there obstacles preventing you from taking any of these actions? If so, what are they? _____

_____

_____

_____

Consider another quotation:

"The very characteristics that make a woman most successful in family roles—the capacity to take pleasure in family-centered, repetitive activities, to sustain and support members of the family rather than pursuing her own goals, to enhance relationships through boundaryless empathy—these are all antithetical to success in the bounded, manipulative, competitive, rational, and egocentric world of work. Because they are not highly motivated and because they are uncertain about what is normal or desirable, many women do not work. Even those who do continue to feel psychologically responsible for the maintenance of the family and are unwilling to jeopardize family relationships. Most work at jobs that contribute to family vacations, college fees, or the general family budget. Even women who pursue a career or profession, rather than merely holding a meaningless job, assume the responsibility for two major, demanding roles. Rather than make this commitment, many women professionalize their voluntary or club activities, bringing qualities of aggression, competitiveness, and organizing skills to these 'safer' activities."

BARDWICK AND DOUVAN
Ambivalence: The Socialization of Women*

*©1971 by Basic Books, Inc., Publishers, New York

What do you think about this passage? What about it is like you? _____

_____

What about it is not like you? _____

_____

To get another look at yourself you might complete the following exercise.

I'm more like this than that

Put a check next to the descriptions that apply to you.

I'm more:

☐ cautious than inclined to take risks

☐ intuitive than objective

☐ dependent than independent

☐ influenced by what others think than by what I think

☐ feeling than rational

☐ passive than aggressive

☐ quiet than assertive

Supply some of your own descriptions:

☐

☐

☐

What does your "more than" profile tell you about yourself? _____

_____

_____

Are you satisfied with your profile? Why? _____

_____

_____

How does your profile differ from or resemble others you know?

A friend _____

Husband _____

Father _____

Mother _____

Unsuccessful woman _____

Successful woman _____

Unsuccessful man _____

Successful man _____

Have any of the items in your profile hindered your decision-making? Explain.

_____

_____

Consider new options ... new roles

Why wouldn't you want to be a:

Lawyer_____

Secretary_____

Carpenter_____

Doctor_____

Teacher_____

Choreographer_____

Mixologist_____

Prostitute_____

Stockbroker_____

Sales manager_____

Mechanic_____

Travel agent_____

Computer programmer_____

Dancer_____

Writer_____

Spotter_____

Banker_____

Housewife_____

Accountant_____

Mother_____

Plumber_____

Chef_____

Designer_____

Stripper_____

Are you satisfied with your reasons? Why?_____
_____

At this point in your life can you do anything about it?_____
_____

Is there anything on the above list that you would like to be if something about it could be different, if there were some characteristic of the career you could change?

What You'd Like to Be	What You'd Change Before You Took Action
_____	_____
_____	_____
_____	_____
_____	_____

What do the changes you'd want to make tell you about yourself?
_____
_____

94

 **CHECKPOINT**

The decisions you make are you

Remember, a decision is an action. An action is something you do.
It is a commitment of limited resources that you can never get back.
Try to think of the actions of some people you know. What actions have
they taken that tell you something about them?

Person	Action(s)	How Action Describes Person In Some Way
Favorite famous person	_____	_____
	_____	_____
Someone you dislike	_____	_____
	_____	_____
Best male friend	_____	_____
	_____	_____
Best female friend	_____	_____
	_____	_____
A successful person	_____	_____
	_____	_____
Employer or boss	_____	_____
	_____	_____
Other person:		
_____	_____	_____
_____	_____	_____
_____	_____	_____
_____	_____	_____
_____	_____	_____

What are you capable of doing out in this world?

A thorough self-analysis includes a focus on the skills and abilities, including personal skills and attributes, you can bring to a job.

The first step in analyzing skills and abilities is to list experiences you have had, including volunteer experiences, college courses, and primary activities carried out in any job you have held. As a second step, you should describe the abilities resulting from those experiences. Skills used in raising a family, such as planning and organizing skills, are needed in paid work environments as well.

Practice describing your experiences, both personal and academic, in terms of the abilities and skills involved by completing the chart opposite.

List successful experiences on the chart and analyze each of them to determine the skills and competencies required in each. Check each of the skills that apply to the experiences you have had.

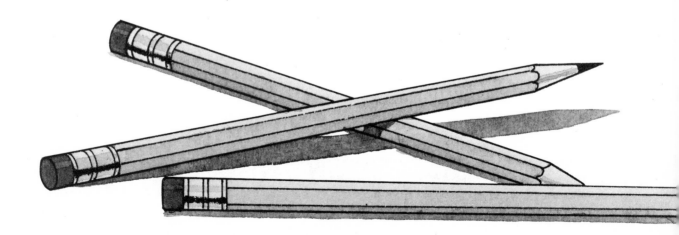

		Managing	Organizing	Selling	Persuading	Analyzing	Writing	Mechanical	Artistic	Precision (detail)	Human-relations	Computational
Paid work												
Nonpaid work												
Education												
Hobbies/leisure												

Skills and Competencies

Relating your skills and competencies to a goal you'd like to attain

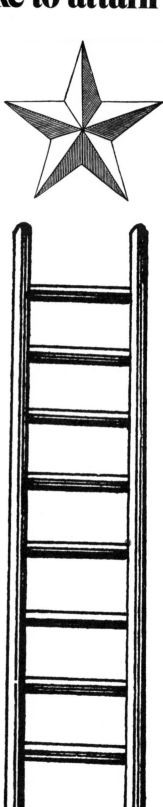

List your skills and competencies and show how they relate to several career alternatives that you might want to pursue.

Skills and competencies

_____

_____

_____

Career alternative and relationship to skills and competencies

_____

_____

_____

_____

_____

Now try to determine what competencies or skills you think you are missing for each career alternative.

Career alternative

_____

_____

_____

Missing skill or competency

_____

_____

_____

What additional information do you need relating to skills or competencies or to the career alternatives you'd like to pursue?

Information needed

_____

_____

_____

Why needed

_____

_____

_____

What action can you take to move closer to the alternatives you want?

Action

_____

_____

_____

When will you take this action?

_____

_____

_____

Getting what you want... setting up a program for action

The exercise that follows calls for your active participation in certain kinds of tasks you may face in job-hunting. Although these tasks deal primarily with job-hunting, you may find the exercise beneficial if you are developing a plan of action to carry out other decisions, such as returning to school or choosing a college major.

There are three major barriers that women often face in looking for a job. *Attitudinal barriers* involve attitudes or perceptions that you, your family, society, or employers may have about women and work. For example, you may run into prejudices about the kinds of jobs women should have or about women with children working at all. *Situational barriers* involve such things as financial difficulties, inadequate child-care facilities, and/or limited mobility. *Institutional barriers* involve red tape in filling out application forms, writing resumes, taking qualification tests, etc. Completing the six job-hunting tasks in this simulation game will involve more decision-making on your part as you face and overcome some of these barriers.

STEP 1

When undertaking any important task, a woman should consciously evaluate herself to determine clearly who she is, what she values, and what her objectives are. Before beginning this simulated job hunting exercise, review the exercises you completed previously in "Who Are You?" by responding to the questions below.

What are your values in order of importance?_____

_____

_____

What are your family responsibilities?_____

_____

_____

What are your skills and abilities?_____

_____

_____

Which of your personal characteristics or qualities do you consider valuable or important?_____

_____

_____

What are some of your long-range and short-range goals? Be specific.

_____

_____

_____

STEP 2

Six tasks are given in the following pages: Building Your Self-Confidence, The Family Conference, The Resume, The Job Campaign, The Employment Application, and The Interview.

If you are working with this book by yourself, the tasks should be carried out in your real-life situation. If possible, you should complete all six tasks within two weeks. As you complete Tasks II-VI, respond to the questions at the end of the description. Before beginning a task read it through carefully. Each is to be completed in the order given.

If you are in a group, you may want to try role-playing some of the tasks.

Task I — Building Your Self-Confidence

As you begin to make plans to take action, you may become anxious about what others may think of those plans, what you might do wrong, and what might happen after you take action. This applies whether you are planning an interview, thinking about being assertive, signing up to take an entrance examination, or filling out an employment application. Although anxiety is not "bad" in itself, too much anxiety may cause you to complete the task with greater difficulty and with less satisfying results. Sometimes women do not do things that could lead to their greater happiness and satisfaction because of that initial anxiety.

To focus more clearly on your positive aspects in order to increase your self-confidence and decrease your anxiety, try the following exercise. Take several three by five cards and write on each card a positive feature about your life and/or yourself. Examples might be "I'm proud of being able to make my own clothes" or "I'm proud of handling all arrangements for the church bazaar." Try to identify three positive qualities at first. Then select an activity you enjoy doing each day (having a cup of coffee each morning with a magazine, watching TV) and before you do that, read over each card and fill out at least one new one. Continue adding to your list of positive qualities for a week. Read over your cards daily. The qualities must be realistic to be effective, so avoid generalizations like "I'm a good person." Try to focus on specific positive things.

Task II

The Family Conference

Consult your family (parents, husband, or husband and children) or significant other people (boy friend, fiance, close friend) about your plans for work or some other decision. Letting your family or others contribute to your thinking or planning can produce positive benefits for you in the form of concrete ideas and support. It is possible that your family may not understand or accept your plans and ideas, and you may become discouraged as you try to convince them how important work can be for you and for them. If you let them participate in your thinking and follow you through the various steps of seeking a job, you are more likely to elicit their interest and cooperation. Your task is first to formulate your goals and objectives as you perceive them, and second to present them to your family or others.

What time and place did you choose for presenting your goals and objectives?

_____

_____

_____

_____

What goals and plans did you present?_____

_____

_____

_____

Did you get the response you expected? Explain._____

_____

_____

_____

Did any new ideas emerge for you? Explain._____

_____

_____

_____

Task III — The Resume

Your task will be to construct two resumes that can persuade an employer to interview you. A resume is a concise statement of what you have to offer an employer. The format of a resume depends on whether the intent is to stress work, experience, education, skills or abilities, or potential. In the following exercise you are to construct one resume that places emphasis on your skills and abilities and another that places emphasis on your work experience. Always play up your strengths and write your resume in a way that shows you are interested in an employer's concerns.

Use the following instructions as a guide:

- The resume must be typed and placed on the page so it can be read easily. Keep the length to one page. Put your name, address, and telephone number at the top.

- Then list your job objective. Naming a specific job on the resume could limit your opportunities. Either indicate a field of interest such as "sales" or "personnel" or synthesize your qualifications into one statement, for example "A position that demands above average communication skills and human-relations skills." Avoid generalities such as "A challenging position leading to increased responsibility."

Resume 1

After you have listed your job objective, you are ready to construct an analytical resume that stresses your skills or abilities. Refer to the exercise "What Are You Capable of Doing out in This World?" beginning on page 96. Select two or three skills or accomplishments you wish to highlight and organize them under the heading *Qualifications*. For example:

"Human-relations skills. My summer jobs have always involved dealing with people on a public level: hostess and camp counselor for a conference center, waitress in a restaurant, sales clerk in a retail store, and receptionist in a doctor's office and finance company. These experiences have helped me develop a pleasant manner in dealing with people, including irate customers."

Continue with the headings *Employers* (list job title, employer, and dates of employment), *Education* and *Personal Information* (honors, awards, hobbies, activities, etc.).

As a final entry, list names and addresses of references or indicate that references are available on request.

Resume 2

This resume will stress your work experience. After you have listed your job objective, organize the jobs you have held, with duties briefly described, under the heading *Work History*. Don't forget volunteer experiences. For example:

"File clerk at First National Bank and Trust Company, August 1969–June 1975. Filed checks, helped with customers in statement department, balanced statements, worked as a relief teller."

Continue with headings *Education* and *Personal Information* (honors, awards, activities, etc.)

As a final entry, list names and addresses of references or indicate that references are available on request.

You should experiment with several drafts of your resume to assure that each entry is readable and understandable. As a final step, have a friend read and criticize it. Which resume sells you most persuasively? Why?

_____

_____

_____

How will the experience of developing a resume help you in job hunting?

_____

_____

_____

What decision-making skills did you use in preparing your resume?

_____

_____

_____

Task IV The Job Campaign

A problem some women face, particularly married women, is lack of mobility. It can be extremely frustrating or discouraging to have the training or ability for a kind of work that is not available, or seemingly not available, within reasonable distance of your home and family. For this task, assume that because of your life circumstances or by choice, you are limited in job-hunting to only a certain geographical area. Your task is to develop a plan for job-hunting within this limited area. Identify the type of geographical area to which you will be limited. A city? A small town? A rural area? Then list the employers within that area who might need the skills you described in your resume. Consider the following resources:

- **Newspaper want-ads**
- **Telephone directory**
- **Local library**
- **College placement office**
- **State employment office**
- **Professional publications**
- **College placement annual**
- **Personal contacts**
- **Job placement agencies**

List three things you can do to help determine which of these employers you would be most interested in applying to. Describe how you will initiate contact with the employer having the greatest potential employment opportunities for you. By referral from a college placement or state employment office? By letter of application? By phone call? By other means?

What decision-making skills did you use in this task?_____

_____

_____

Task V — The Employment Application

Examining the list you compiled in Task IV, select an employer you are interested in and pick up an employment application, or go to the employer's office and fill out the application.

The employment application is a main factor in determining which applicants will be called for a job interview. For this reason, all blanks must be filled out carefully. If you take the application home with you, work out your answers on another piece of paper and neatly transfer the information on the application form. If you plan to complete the application at the office, take a written list of facts with you. Be positive. Play up your strengths and play down your weaknesses. For example, if the application asks you to list your skills, do not leave that blank. Refer to the exercise "What Are You Capable of Doing out in This World?" (page 96) and list the skills that emerged from an analysis of your past experiences, education, etc.

Task VI — The Interview

Before you go to an interview, you should be prepared in three basic areas. First find out what goes on in a job interview. Your local library will have books and other materials that should be helpful. Second, find out as much as possible about the employer (company, government agency, or education institution) you will have the interview with. Third, be ready to present clearly your career objectives and your qualifications.

For this task, your interview is with the employer you selected in Task V. You have carefully prepared for the interview and feel this employer may have just the job that fits your objectives. The interviewer describes a job and indicates that it is the only one available for a woman. The job is considerably below what you know you are qualified to do. Describe how you would handle the interview.

How did you feel when the interviewer said this was the only job available for a woman?_____

_____

What was your immediate response?_____

_____

What was the outcome for you?_____

_____

Identify the barrier(s) involved in each of the six tasks._____

_____

Where do you go from here?

Once you have decided to make a change in your life, you may leave those areas where traditionally you have support. You must now look for support in other places.

You have to look to other women who are experiencing the same thing or who have already gone through it. Many men are aware too of the difficulties women face. Sometimes your support may come from your family or from women you have read about. Be willing to take a risk and tell other women how you feel.

And finally, try not to challenge the validity of another's choice simply to strengthen support for your own. Remember, the "rightness" or "wrongness" of a decision has to be judged according to each person's individual circumstance.

You may not be ready to go off and make all your important decisions at this point, but perhaps you are better able to start moving toward what you want in life. For some women, any movement will be a big and positive change; others may consider a greater commitment of resources possible at this point. In any case, it's your life, and your choices will shape the rest of your life.

Try the final exercise on the next page and see if you can start to take action.

The time is <u>now</u>: Your action plan

1. Your critical decision: _____

2. Why is it critical? _____
_____

3. What do you want the results to be? _____
_____
_____

4. What alternatives have you identified? _____
_____
_____
_____

5. What outcomes, good and bad, might occur if you pursue your alternatives?
_____
_____
_____

6. What things do you value in those outcomes? What makes them desirable?
_____
_____
_____

7. What action or actions will you take? _____
_____
_____
_____

8. When? _____

Bibliography

Alberti, R. E., and Emmons, M. L. *Your Perfect Right: A Guide to Assertive Behavior.* San Luis Obispo, Calif.: IMPACT, 1974

Allen, D. *The Price of Women.* New York: Jarrow Press, Inc., 1971

Altbach, E. H. *From Feminism to Liberation.* Cambridge, Mass.: Schenkman Publishing Co., Inc., 1971

Bardwick, J. M. *Psychology of Women.* New York: Harper & Row, 1971

Bardwick, J. M. and Douvan, E. "Ambivalence: The Socialization of Women." In V. Gornick and B. K. Moran (Editors), *Woman in Sexist Society: Studies in Power and Powerlessness.* New York: Basic Books, 1971

Bem, S. L., and Bem, D. J. *Training the Woman to Know Her Place: The Social Antecedents of Women in the World of Work.* Harrisburg, Pa.: Pennsylvania Department of Education, 1974

Berkley, E. P. "Women in Architecture." *Forum,* September 1972

Bernard, J. S. *Women and the Public Interest.* Chicago: Aldine-Atherton, Inc., 1971

Bird, C. *Born Female.* New York: David McKay Company, Inc., 1970

Bird, C. *Everything a Woman Needs to Know to Get Paid What She's Worth.* New York: David McKay Company, Inc., 1973

Black, J. H. "Conceptions of Sex Role: Some Cross-Cultural and Longitudinal Perspectives." *American Psychologist,* June 1973, pp. 512-526

Blai, B., Jr. "Job Satisfaction and Work Values for Women." *Journal of the National Association of Women Deans, Administrators, and Counselors,* 1974, Vol. 37, No. 4, pp. 151-157

Bolles, R. N. *What Color Is Your Parachute?* Berkeley, Calif.: Ten Speed Press, 1972

Boserup, E. *Woman's Role in Economic Development.* London: George Allen and Unwin Ltd., 1970

Briggs, N. "Women Apprentices: Removing the Barriers." *Manpower,* 1974, Vol. 6, No. 12, pp. 3-11

Business and Professional Women's Foundation, *Career Counseling: New Perspectives for Women and Girls.* A Selected Annotated Bibliography. Washington, D.C.: Author, 1972

Catalyst. *Self-Guidance Series.* New York: 1973

Catalyst. *Education Opportunities Series.* New York: 1973

Catalyst. *Career Opportunities Series.* New York: 1973

Chafe, W. H. *The American Woman: Her Changing Social, Economic, and Political Roles, 1920-1970.* New York: Oxford University Press, 1972

Chisholm, ©. *Unbought and Unbossed.* Boston: Houghton Mifflin Company, 1970

Cook, B. "Women's Search for 'A Way of Becoming.'" *Journal of the National Association of Women Deans and Counselors,* 1970, Vol. 34, No. 1, pp. 23-27

Daniels, A. K. *A Survey of Research Concerns on Women's Issues.* Project on the Status and Education of Women. Washington, D.C.: Association of American Colleges, 1975

deBeauvoir, S. *The Second Sex.* New York: Alfred A. Knopf, 1953

DeCrow, K. *The Young Woman's Guide to Liberation.* Indianapolis, Ind.: Pegasus, 1971

Edwards, L. R., et al. *Woman: An Issue.* Boston: Little, Brown and Co., 1972

Farber, S. M. *The Challenge to Women.* New York: Basic Books, Inc., 1966

Ferriss, A. L. *Indicators of Trends in the Status of American Women.* New York: Russell Sage Foundation, 1971

Fitzgerald, L., and Harmon, L. (Guest Editors). Special Issue: *Counseling Women. The Counseling Psychologist,* 1973, Vol. 4, No. 1, pp. 1-131

Flexner, E. *Century of Struggle: The Woman's Rights Movement in the United States.* Cambridge, Mass.: The Belknap Press of Harvard University Press, 1959

Friedan, B. *The Feminine Mystique.* New York: W. W. Norton & Company, Inc., 1963

Friedman, S., and Schwartz, L. C. *No Experience Necessary: A Guide to Employment For the Female Liberal Arts Graduate.* Garden City, N.Y.: Dell Publishing Company, 1971

Fuller, T. *Gnomologia: Adagies, Proverbs, Wise Sentiments, and Witty Sayings, Ancient and Modern, Foreign and British.* London: 1732

Furniss, W., and Graham, P. A. *Women in Higher Education.* Washington, D.C.: American Council on Education, 1974

Gardner, B. B. "The Awakening of the Blue Collar Woman." *Intellectual Digest,* March 1974, pp. 17-19

Garskof, M. H. (Editor). *Roles Women Play: Readings toward Women's Liberation.* Belmont, Calif.: Brooks/Cole Publishing Co., 1971

*****Gelatt, H. B., Varenhorst, Barbara, Carey, Richard, and Miller, Gordon P.** *Decisions and Outcomes: A Leader's Guide.* New York: College Entrance Examination Board, 1973

Gillotti, S. S., Schifter, M. H., and Schwartz, F. N. *How to Go to Work When Your Husband Is Against It, Your Children Aren't Old Enough, and There's Nothing You Can Do Anyhow* (A Catalyst Publication). New York: Simon & Schuster, 1972

Ginzberg E., and Yohalem, A. M. *Corporate Lib — Women's Challenge to Management.* Baltimore, Md.: The Johns Hopkins University Press, 1973

Greer, G. *The Female Eunuch.* London: MacGibbon and Kee Ltd., 1970

*References of special interest to leaders of decision-making groups.

107

Guttman, M. A. (Editor). *Women and ACES: Perspectives and Issues.* Washington, D.C.: Commission for Women, Association for Counselor Education and Supervision, 1974

Harkness, G. *Women in Church and Society.* Nashville, Tenn.: Abingdon Press, 1972

Harris, Janet. *A Single Standard.* New York: McGraw-Hill Book Co., 1971

*Hawley, R. C., and Hawley, I. L. *A Handbook of Activities for Personal and Social Growth.* Amherst, Mass.: Education Research Associates, 1975

Henderson, J. G., and Henderson, A. D. *Ms. Goes to College.* Carbondale, Ill.: Southern Illinois University Press, 1975

Herman, M. H., and Sedlocek, W. E. "Career Orientation of High School and University Women." *Journal of the National Association of Women Deans, Administrators, and Counselors,* 1974, Vol. 37, No. 4, pp. 161-166

Hole, J., and Levine, E. *Rebirth of Feminism.* New York: Quadrangle Books, Inc., 1971

Horner, M., "Fail: Bright Women." *Psychology Today,* 1969, Vol. 3, No. 6, pp. 36-38

House, E., and Katzell, M. (Editors). *Facilitating Career Development for Girls and Women.* Monograph of the National Vocational Guidance Association. Washington, D.C.: American Personnel and Guidance Association, 1975

Huber, J. (Editor). Special Issue: *Changing Women in a Changing Society. American Journal of Sociology,* 1973, Vol. 78

IMPACT. ERIC Counseling and Personnel Services Information Center, The University of Michigan, 1974, Vol. 3, No. 2, pp. 31-34

*Jakubowski-Spector, P. "Facilitating the Growth of Women through Assertive Training." *The Counseling Psychologist,* 1973, Vol. 4, No. 1, pp. 75-86

*Jakubowski-Spector, P. *An Introduction to Assertive Training Procedures for Women.* Washington, D.C.: American Personnel and Guidance Association, 1973

*Jakubowski-Spector, P. "Self-Assertion Training Procedures for Women." In D. Carter and E. Rawlings (Editors), *Psychotherapy for Women: Treatment towards Equality.* Springfield, Ill.: Charles Thomas, in press, 1975

Janeway, E. *Man's World, Woman's Place: A Study in Social Mythology.* New York: William Morrow and Company, Inc., 1971

Jongeward, D., and Scott, D. *Affirmative Action for Women: A Practical Guide.* Reading, Mass.: Addison-Wesley Publishing Company, 1974

Kanowitz, L. *Women and the Law: The Unfinished Revolution,* Albuquerque, N. M.: University of New Mexico Press, 1969

Kellen, K. *The Coming Age of Woman Power.* New York: Peter H. Wyden, Inc., 1972

Knox, B. S. *Trends in the Counseling of Women in Higher Education 1957-1973.* Ruth Strong Research Award Monograph Series: No. 1. Washington, D.C.: National Association for Women Deans, Administrators, and Counselors, July 1975

Komisar, L. *The New Feminism.* New York: Franklin Watts, Inc., 1971

Kraditor, A. S. *Up from the Pedestal.* Chicago: Quadrangle Books, Inc., 1968

Kreps, J. M. *Sex in the Marketplace: American Women at Work.* Baltimore, Md.: The Johns Hopkins Press, 1971

Krohn, M. H. *Planning for Career Options.* New York: Catalyst, 1975

Lawrence, M. *School of Femininity.* Port Washington, N.Y.: Kennikat Press, 1966. Reprint of 1936 edition. Published in England as *We Write As Women*

Lerner, G. *The Woman in American History.* Reading, Mass.: Addison-Wesley Publishing Co., 1971

Lewis, E. C. *Developing Woman's Potential.* Ames, Iowa: Iowa State University Press, 1968

Lewis, J. A. (Guest Editor). Special Issue: *Women and Counselors. The Personnel and Guidance Journal,* 1972, Vol. 51, No. 2, pp. 81-160

Lifton, R. J. *The Woman in America.* Boston: Houghton-Mifflin Co., 1965

Loring, R. *Breakthrough: Women into Management.* New York: Van Nostrand Reinhold Company, 1972

McBee, M. L., and Blake, K. A. *The American Woman: Who Will She Be?* Beverly Hills, Calif.: Glencoe Press, 1974

McClelland, D. "Opening Job Doors for Mature Women." *Manpower,* 1973, Vol. 5, No. 8, pp. 8-12

McGrath, L. P., and Scobey, J. *Creative Careers for Women: A Handbook for Part-time Jobs.* Essandess Special Edition. New York: Simon & Schuster, 1968

Mailer, N. *The Prisoner of Sex.* Boston: Little, Brown and Co., 1971

Marine, G. *A Male Guide to Women's Liberation.* New York: Holt, Rinehart and Winston, 1972

Marston, W. M., *Wonder Woman.* New York: Holt, Rinehart and Winston, 1972

Mednick, M. S. and Tangri, S. S. (Editors). Special Issue: *New Perspectives on Women. Journal of Social Issues,* 1972, Vol. 28

Merriam, E. *Growing Up Female in America.* Garden City, N.Y.: Doubleday and Co., Inc., 1971

Millett, K. *Sexual Politics.* Garden City, N.Y.: Doubleday and Co., Inc., 1971

Mitchell, J. S. *I Can Be Anything: Careers and Colleges for Young Women.* New York: College Entrance Examination Board, 1975

Montagu, A. *The Natural Superiority of Women.* Revised edition. New York: The Macmillan Co., 1968

Notes from the Second Year: Women's Liberation: Major Writings of the Radical Feminists. New York: Radical Feminism, 1970

Notes From the Third Year: Women's Liberation. New York: Radical Feminism, 1971

Oliver, L. W. "The Relationship of Parental Attitudes and Parent Identification to Career and Homemaking Orientation in College Women." *Journal of Vocational Behavior,* 1975, Vol. 7, No. 1, pp. 1-12

O'Neill, W. L. *Everyone Was Brave.* Chicago: Quadrangle Books, Inc., 1969

Opportunities for Women in Higher Education. A Report and Recommendations by the Carnegie Commission on Higher Education. New York: 1973

Parrish, J. B. "Women, Careers and Counseling: The New Era." *Journal of the National Association of Women Deans, Administrators, and Counselors,* 1974, Vol. 38, No. 1, pp. 11-19

Percy, S. "A Trailblazer Looks Back." *Manpower,* 1973, Vol. 5, No. 8, pp. 22-23

*Pfeiffer, J. W., and Jones, J. E. *Structured Experiences for Human Relations Training.* La Jolla, Calif.: University Associates, Vol. 1-4, 1974

Phelps, S., and Austin, N. The Assertive Woman. Fredericksburg, Va.: IMPACT, 1975

Political and Economic Planning. Women in Top Jobs: Four Studies in Achievement. London: George Allen and Unwin Ltd., 1971

Prentice, B. *The Back to Work Handbook for Housewives: 500 Job and Career Ideas.* New York: Collier Books, 1971

Reeves, N. *Womankind: Beyond the Stereotypes.* Chicago: Aldine-Atherton, Inc., 1971

Reische, D. L. *Women and Society.* New York: H. W. Wilson Co., 1972

Riegel, R. E. *American Feminists.* Lawrence, Kans.: University of Kansas Press, 1963

Robins, J. *Handbook of Women's Liberation.* North Hollywood, Calif.: NOW Library Press, 1970

Rover, C. *Love, Morals and the Feminists.* London: Routledge and Kegan Paul, 1970

Sandler, B. "Women: The Last Minority." *Journal of College Placement,* December 1971-January 1972, Vol. 32, p. 49

Schindler-Rainman, E. "Are Values Out of Style?" *Journal of the National Association of Women Deans and Counselors,* 1970, Vol. 34, No. 1, pp. 18-22

Scott, A. F. *Women in American Life: Selected Readings.* Boston: Houghton-Mifflin Company, 1970

Scott, A. F. (Editor). *What Is Happening to American Women.* Atlanta, Ga.: SNPA Foundation Seminar Books, 1970

Sharma, V. "Continuing Education and Counseling for Women: Some Problems and Suggestions." In M. J. Guttman (Editor), *Women and ACES: Perspectives and Issues.* Washington, D.C.: Commission for Women, Association for Counselor Education and Supervision, 1974, p. 100

*Simon, S. B., Howe, L. W., and Kirschenbaum, H. *Values Clarification. A Handbook of Practical Strategies for Teachers and Students.* New York: Hart Publishing Company, 1972

Smith, M. J. *When I Say No I Feel Guilty.* New York: The Dial Press, 1975

Sochen, J. *The New Woman.* New York: Quadrangle Books, Inc., 1972

Splaner, S. *Nontraditional Careers for Women.* New York: Julian Messner, 1974

Stambler, S. *Women's Liberation: Blueprint for the Future.* New York: Ace Books, 1970

Sullivan, V. (Compiler). *Plays by and about Women.* New York: Random House, 1973

Tanner, L. B. *Voices from Women's Liberation.* New York: New American Library, Inc., 1970

Theodore, A. (Editor) *The Professional Woman.* Cambridge, Mass.: Schenkman Publishing Company, Inc., 1971

Tibbetts, S. L. "Sex Role Stereotyping: Why Women Discriminate Against Themselves." *Journal of the National Association for Women Deans, Administrators, and Counselors,* 1975, Vol. 38, No. 4, pp. 177-183

Trahey, J. *Harper's Bazaar: 100 Years of the American Female.* New York: Random House, 1967

United Nations Secretary-General (Thant). *Participation of Women in the Economic and Social Development of Their Countries.* New York: United Nations Publications, 1970

U.S. Congress, Committee on Education and Labor. *Discrimination Against Women: Congressional Hearings on Equal Rights in Education and Employment.* New York: R. R. Bowker Co., 1973

U.S. Government Printing Office. "Women in Defense." *Commander's Digest,* Vol. 14, 1973

U.S. President's Commission on the Status of Women. *American Women.* New York: Charles Scribner's Sons, 1965

Voices of the New Feminism. Boston: Beacon Press, 1970

Wolkon, K. A. *Counseling Girls and Women: A Guide for Jewish and Other Minority Women.* Washington, D. C.: B'nai B'rith Career and Counseling Service, 1973

Women in Action. Ann Arbor, Mich.: Center for Continuing Education of Women, The University of Michigan, 1969

Women's Centers: Where Are They? Project on the Status and Education of Women. Washington, D. C.: Association of American Colleges, 1974

Women's Liberation and the Church. New York: Association Press, 1970

Wortis, H., and Rabinowitz, C. *The Women's Movement: Social and Psychological Perspectives.* New York: AMS Press, Inc., 1972

Women's centers: Where are they?

PREPARED BY THE PROJECT ON THE STATUS AND EDUCATION OF WOMEN

ALABAMA

Women's Center
Office of Women's Affairs
Miles College
5500 Avenue G
Birmingham 35208

The Association for New Women
P.O. Box U-27
307 Gaillard Drive
Mobile 36688

ALASKA

Fairbanks Women's Coop
University of Alaska
c/o Student Activities
Fairbanks 99701

ARIZONA

Associated Women Students
Jeanne Rice, AWS President
Arizona State University
Memorial Union 252-C
Tempe 85281
602/965-3438

Tempe Women's Center
1414 S. McAllister
Tempe 85281
602/968-0743

Tucson's Women's Center
838 North 4th Avenue
Tucson 85705

Women's Collective
829 N. 5th Avenue
Tucson 85705
602/792-1890

ARKANSAS

Women's Ctr. of Fayetteville
Mary Cochran, Billie Traynam,
   Nancy Sindon
University of Arkansas
902 W. Maple Street
Fayetteville 72701

CALIFORNIA

Women's Studies Program
c/o Kathy Marshall
Calif. State University—Humboldt
Arcata 95521

**Center for Continuing Ed. for
   Women & Women's Ctr.**
Diana Gong
Univ. of Ca.—Berkeley
Building T-9, Room 100
Berkeley 94720
415/642-4786

Female Liberation
Univ. of Ca.—Berkeley
516 Eshelman Hall
Berkeley 94720

Men's Center
2700 Bancroft Way
Berkeley 94704
415/845-4823

Women's Center
Addison Street
Berkeley 94720

Women's Center
Graduate Theological Union
2378 Virginia Avenue
Berkeley 94709

Women's Coffee House
Unitas House
2700 Bancroft
Berkeley 94704

Women's Center
2134 Allston (downstairs)
Berkeley 94704
415/548-4343

Chico Women's Center
c/o Marilyn Murphy
932 Alder Street
Chico 95926

Women's Studies Center
Calif. State Univ.—Chico
Chico 95926

Women's Center
Orange Coast College
2701 Fairview Road
Costa Mesa 92626

Women's Center Office—Costa Mesa
1926 Placentia #15
Costa Mesa 92627

Davis Women's Center
Sandi McCubbin, Coordinator
Univ. of Calif.—Davis TB-124
Davis 95616

Women's Educational Center
c/o Cindi Conway
Calif. State College of Dominguez Hills
1000 East Victoria
Dominguez Hills 90246

Women's Task Force
c/o Hessel Flitter
Ohlone College
P.O. Box 909
Fremont 94537

Women's Center
Doris N. Deakins,
   Assoc. Dean of Students
Fresno City College
1101 University Avenue
Fresno 93741
209/262-4721

Women's Center
c/o Diane Reeves
Calif. State Univ.
Fullerton 92634

**Women's Education Program
   Director, Women's Ctr.**
c/o Kathleen M. Zanger
Ganilan Community College
5055 Santa Teresa
Gilroy 95020

Women's Center
c/o Pat Lienhard
Glendale Community College
1500 N. Verdugo Road
Glendale 91208

Isla Vista Women's Center
6504 Pardall Road, #2
Goleta 93017

Women's Center
Lynne Tuscono
Univ. of Calif.—Irvine
c/o Community Projects Office
Irvine 92664

Women's Opportunities Center
Univ. of Calif.—Irvine Extension
Irvine 92664
714/833-7128

Women's Programs—Ext.
Dr. Mary Lindenstein Walshok
Univ. of Calif. Ext.
P.O. Box 109
La Jolla 92037

Women's Center
Continuing Ed. Center for Women
Beverly O'Neill, Director
Long Beach City College
4901 E. Carson Blvd.
Long Beach 90815

Women's Center
c/o Karen Johnson
Calif. State Univ.
6407 Bayard Street
Long Beach 90815

Center for Women's Studies
Lucille Todd, Director
Pepperine University
1121 W. 79th Street
Los Angeles 90044

The Project on the Status and Education of Women of the Association of American Colleges began operations in September of 1971. The Project provides a clearinghouse of information concerning women in education and works with institutions, government agencies, and other associations and programs affecting women in higher education. The Project is funded by the Carnegie Corporation of New York, the Danforth Foundation, and the Exxon Education Foundation. Publication of these materials does not necessarily constitute endorsement by AAC or any of the foundations which fund the Project.

Los Angeles Women's Liberation Center
c/o Margo Miller
746 S. Crenshaw
Los Angeles 90005
213/936-7219

Womanspace
11007 Venice Blvd.
Los Angeles 90034

Women's Resource Center
Carol Adams, Director
U.C.L.A.—Powell Library, Room 90
405 Hilgard Avenue
Los Angeles 90024
213/825-3945

Women's Center
P.O. Box 1501
Monterey 93940

YWCA of Los Angeles
East Valley Center
5903 Laurel Canyon Blvd.
North Hollywood 91607

Women's Studies Research Institute
Attn: Myra Strober
Asst. Professor of Economics
Stanford University
Graduate School of Business
Palo Alto 94305

**Women's Information and
 Counseling Center**
c/o Stephanie Coles
Contra Costa College
405 Santa Fe Avenue
Point Richmond 94801

Women's Center
Diane LeBow, Advisor
Canada College
4200 Farm Hill Blvd.
Redwood City 94061

Riverside Women's Center
3122 Panorama Street
Riverside 92506

Women's Center
4459-2 Orange Grove
Riverside 92501

Women's Survival Center
Dr. Janice Wilson, Director
Calif. State Univ.—Sonoma
1801 E. Cotati Avenue
Rohnert Park 94928

Continuing Ed. for Women
Sacramento State University
Sacramento 95819

Sacramento Women's Center
YWCA Building
17th and "L"
Sacramento 95819

Women's Studies—CSUS
California State U.—Sacramento
6000 J Street
Sacramento 95819

**Monterey County Peace Center
 (Women's Center)**
Box 1364
Salina 93901

Valice
205 Laurel Avenue
San Anselmo 94960

Woman's Way
412 Red Hill Avenue, Suite 9
San Anselmo 94960

Center for Women's Studies and Services
Calif. State U.
908 F Street
San Diego 92101

Center for Women's Studies and Services
4004 39th Street
San Diego 92105

Women's Liberation
Aztec Center, Organizational Center
San Diego State College
San Diego 92105

American Indian Women's Center
227 Valencia
San Francisco 94103

**Bay Area Consortium of Continuing
 Ed. of Women**
Dr. Mary Janet, Prof. of Chemistry
Lone Mountain College
San Francisco 94118

Haight-Ashbury Women's Ctr.
#10 Ryan Street
San Francisco 94117

Intersection Women's Night
756 Union Street
San Francisco 94133

San Francisco Women's Switchboard
c/o YWCA
620 Sutter Street
San Francisco 94102
415/771-8212

Women's Center for Creative Counseling
San Francisco: 415/648-1509
San Mateo: 342-0278
Daly City: 756-4736

Women's Legal Center
558 Capp Street
San Francisco 94110

Women's Need Center
558 Clayton Street
San Francisco 94117

San Jose Women's Center
9th & San Carlos Bldg.
San Jose 95114

Women's Center
San Jose State U.
San Jose 95114

Women's Center
Ms. Elizabeth Burdash, Coordinator
College of San Mateo
1700 W. Hillsdale Blvd.
San Mateo 94402

**Women's Center & Emergency
 Housing, YWCA**
1618 Mission Street
San Raphael 94901
415/456-0782

**Feminist Women's Health Center
 of Orange County**
429 S. Sycamore Street
Santa Ana 92701

Continuing Education for Women
c/o Myrtle Blum
Psychology Department
U. of Calif.
Santa Barbara 93107

Women's Center—Santa Cruz
314 Laurel Street
Santa Cruz 95060

Stanford Women's Center
Box 2633
Stanford 94305
321-2300 ext. 314

West Side Women's Center
218 W. Venice Blvd.
Venice 90291
213/823-4774

Women's Center
2914 Grand Canal
Venice 90291

Women's Center
Attn: Angela Lask
El Camino College
16007 Crenshaw Blvd.
Via Torrence 90506

CANADA

Edmonton Women's Centre
9623-103 Avenue
Edmonton, Alberta

Women's Center
11812-95th Street
Edmonton, Alberta

Women's Resource Center
2961-272nd Street
Aldergrove, B.C.

Women's Center
Box 521
Nelson, B.C.

Centre for Continuing Ed.
"Re-Entry Programs for Women"
Attn: Jo Lynne Hoegg
University of British Columbia
Vancouver, B.C.

A Woman's Place
1766 W. Broadway
Vancouver, B.C.

Women's Center
804 Richards Street
Vancouver, B.C.

Women's Centre
511 Carroll Street
Vancouver, B.C.

Women's Center
1029 Douglas Street, #414
Victoria, B.C.

Winnipeg Women's Center
577 Agnes Street
Winnepeg, Manitoba

Women's Liberation
c/o Millie Lamb
#10, 812 Wolseley
Winnipeg, Manitoba

Women's Center
c/o Linda Gow, Y.W.C.A.
27 Wellington Row
St. John, New Brunswick

Women's Place
204 Water Street
St. John's, Newfoundland

Women's Center
c/o Nellie Cournoyea
Inuvik, North West Territories

Women's Bureau
Box 3596, Halifax South
Postal Station, Halifax, Nova Scotia

Joanne Opperman
Wellington, R.R. #1
Grand River, Prince Edward Island

Open Arms Haven for Women
290 James Street North
Near Barton
Hamilton, Ontario

Women's Center
306 Herkimer Street
Hamilton, Ontario

London Women's Resource Center
283 Dufferin Avenue
London, Ontario

Women's Center
136 Lewis Street (rear)
Ottawa, Ontario

Women's Place
366 Water Street
Peterborough, Ontario

Canadian Women's Educational Press
280 Bloor Street West, Room 304
Toronto, Ontario

Deanna White
7 Walmer Road, #1807
Toronto, Ontario

Toronto Women's Center
1267 Queen Street West
Toronto, Ontario

Women and Film
9 A Charles Street West
Toronto, Ontario

Women's Place
31 Dupont Street
Toronto, Ontario

YWCA
21 McGill Street
Toronto, Ontario

Women's Collective
300 ERB Street
Waterloo, Ontario

The Women's Place
968 University Avenue West
Windsor, Ontario

Centre de Femmes
4319 St. Denis
Montreal 131, Quebec

Centre d'information &
de reference pour femmes
3595 St. Urbain
Montreal 131, Quebec
514/842-4781

Women's Center
3764 St. Laurent
Montreal, Quebec

Women's Counselling Service
c/o Susan Mahon
3650 Hutchison Street
Montreal 112, Quebec

Women's Information & Referral Center
3595 Urban
Montreal 131, Quebec

Women's Mobile Information Unit
3641 St. Lawrence Blvd.
Montreal, Quebec

Regina University Women's Center
Student Services Bldg .
Regina University
Regina, Saskatchewan

Women's Center
1 Angus
Regina, Saskatchewan

Women's Center
147 2nd Avenue South
Saskatoon, Saskatchewan

COLORADO

Resource Center for Women
Adams State College
San Luis Ranch
Alamosa 81101

University of Colorado Women's Center
Atn: Darcy Sease
UMC 334
Boulder 80302
443-2211, ext. 7523

Women's Center
1520 Euclid
Boulder 80302

Gay Women's Center
c/o Debby Squires
2460 South Ogden
Denver 80210

Research Center on Women
Loretto Heights College
3001 South Federal Blvd .
Denver 80236

Virginia Neal Blue Center
Colorado Women's College
1800 Pontiac Street
Denver 80220

Women's Center
1452 Pennsylvania #17
Denver 80203

Women's Resource Center
c/o Joann Albright
University of Denver
University Park
Denver 80210

Women's Studies Program
Dr. Barbara Blansett
Metropolitan State College
Denver 80210

Women's Crisis & Information Center
Carol Gillespie, Director
Colorado State University
629 South Howes Street
Ft. Collins 80521
303/493-3888

Women's Research Center
c/o Mary Leonard
Office of Women's Relations
112 Student Services
Colorado State University
Ft. Collins 80521
303/491-6383

Center for Women
Meg Nichols
Mesa College
Mesa Junior College Dist.
Grand Junction 81501

Virginia Neal Blue Women's
Resource Center
c/o Nancy Frank
Southern Colorado State College
Pueblo 81001

CONNECTICUT

Every Woman's Center
YWCA of Greater Bridgeport
Lillie Margaret Lazaruk
968 Fairfield
Bridgeport 06606
203/334-6154

Asnuntuck Community College
Michael J. Moran, Director of
Library Services
P.O. Box 68
Enfield 06082

Women's Center
c/o Barbara Crossea
87 Ridgefield Street
Hartford 06112

Women's Liberation Center
of Greater Hartford, Inc.
Lynn Gall
11 Amity Street
Hartford 06106
203/523-8949

Wesleyan Women's Center
Wesleyan University
High Street
Middletown 06520

Women's Center
115 College Street
Middletown 06457
203/346-4042

Union Theological Women's Center
3438 Yale Station
New Haven 06520

University Women's Organization &
Information Counseling Center
Yale University
215 Park Street
New Haven 06520
203/436-0272

Women's Center
Yale University
Divinity School
Bacon Building
New Haven 06520

Women's Center
198 Elm Street
New Haven 06520

Counseling Center for Women
Ms. Marlene Adelman, Director
Norwalk Community College
33 Wilson Avenue
Norwalk 06854

Women's Liberation Center
11 North Main Street
South Norwalk 06856

Women's Center
Teri Eblen, Donna MacDonnell—Johnson
University of Connecticut
U-8 Student Union
Storrs 06268

Continuing Education for Women
c/o Elizabeth Roper
Univ. of Conn.—Torrington Branch
University Drive
Torrington 06790

DELAWARE
Ed. Services for Women
Mae R. Carter, Program Specialist
University of Delaware
John M. Clayton Hall
Newark 19711
302/738-2211

Women's Center
c/o Episcopal Student Center
University of Delaware
57 East Park Place
Newark 19711

DISTRICT OF COLUMBIA
Black Women's Institute
National Council of Negro Women
1346 Connecticut Avenue N.W.
Washington 20036

Institute for Continuing Education for Women
Dr. Beverly B. Cassara, Acting Director
Federal City College
1424 K Street N.W.
Washington 20001
202/727-2824

Continuing Education for Women
Dr. Ruth Osborn, Assistant Dean
GWU College of General Studies
George Washington University
2029 K Street N.W.
Washington 20006

Trinity College Women's Center
Trinity College
Michigan Avenue N.E.
Washington 20002

Washington Area Women's Center, Inc.
1736 R Street N.W.
Washington 20009
202/232-5145

Women's Center
Catholic University
Michigan Avenue N.E.
Washington 20017

Women's Phone
c/o Community Bookstore
2028 P Street N.W.
Washington 20036

FLORIDA
Women's Commission
Dr. Evelyn Helmich Hireley
University of Miami
Coral Gables 33124

Career Planning for Disadvantaged Women
Ms. Chloe Atkins
Santa Fe Community College
P.O. Box 1530
3000 N.W. 83rd Street
Gainesville 32601

Options (Women's Center)
1825 Hendricks Avenue
Jacksonville 32207
904/398-7728

Council for Continuing Ed. for Women
Betty Kaynor, Coordinator
Miami-Dade Junior College
141 N.E. 3rd Avenue
Miami 33132

Institute for Women
Charlotte R. Tatro, Director
Florida International University
Tamiami Trail
Miami 33144

Women's Information Center
6255 S.W. 69th Street
South Miami 33143

Women's Center
2554-1st Avenue North
St. Petersburg 33713
813/822-8156

Tallahassee Women's Educational & Cultural Center
Debora K. Patterson
Florida State University
212 Mabry Heights, FSU Box 6826
Tallahassee 32306
904/599-4049 or 559-3281

Tampa Women's Center
Box 1350
Tampa 33601

Tampa Women's Center
214 Columbia Drive #3
Tampa 33606

Women's Center
c/o Joyce Davis
3215 Walcraft Road
Tampa 33611

The Women's Center
405 Grand Central Avenue
Tampa 33604

Women's Center
University of South Florida
Student Organizations Office
Box 438 University Center
Tampa 33620

GEORGIA
Atlanta Woman's Center
c/o Jane Kelley
1315 Stillwood Drive N.E.
Atlanta 30306

Women's Center
Midtown YWCA
45-11th Street
Atlanta 30303

HAWAII
Women's Center
University YWCA
1820 University Avenue
Honolulu 96822

Women's Studies
Doris Ladd
University of Hawaii, Manoa
Spalding 252
Honolulu 96822

CEW, University of Hawaii
c/o Marion Saunders
931 University Avenue #205
Honolulu 96914

IDAHO
University of Idaho Women's Center
Jane E. Langenes, Student
Advisory Services
108 Administration Bldg.
Moscow 83843
208/885-6616

Women's Center
Idaho State University
Pocatello 83201

ILLINOIS
Women's Center
c/o Ms. Sue Palmer
Aurora College
Aurora 60507

Carbondale Women's Center
c/o Rita Moss
1202 West Schwartz
Carbondale 62901

Continuing Ed. for Women
Director: Edith C. Spees
Southern Illinois University
Pulliam Hall, Room 110
Carbondale 62901

Women's Center
404 West Walnut
Carbondale 62901

Student Personnel Office for Continuing Ed. for Women
Betty L. Hembrough, Assistant Dean
University of Illinois
130 Student Services
610 East John Street
Champaign 61820
217/333-3137

Chicago Ecumenical Women's Center
c/o Janet H. Miller
5751 South Woodlawn, #111
Chicago 60637

Chicago Women's Liberation Union
852 West Belmont
Chicago 60657
312/348-4300

Ecumenical Women's Center in Chicago
Northside Center
1653 West School
Chicago 60657

Loop Center—YWCA
37 South Wabash Street
Chicago 60603
312/372-6600

M.O.R.E. for Women
5465 South Shore Drive
Chicago 60615

The Sisters Center
Northside Women's Liberation
7071 Glenwood
Chicago 60626

Sister Center
United Church of Rogers Park
Morris at Ashland
Chicago 60626

Women's Center
North Area
1016 North Dearborn Street
Chicago 60610
312/337-4385

Women's Center
Southwest Area
3134 West Marquette Road
Chicago 60629
312/436-3500

Women's Center
South Suburban
45 Plaza, Park Forest
Chicago 60466
312/748-5660

Women's Center
Uptown
4409 North Sheridan Road
Chicago 60640
312/561-6737

Women's Center
West Side
5082 West Jackson Blvd., 2nd floor
Chicago 60644
312/379-8332

Women's Center
6200 South Drexel Street
Chicago 60637
312/955-3100

Women's Center
3322 North Halsted Street
Chicago 60657
312/935-4270

Women's Center
436 East 39th Street
Chicago 60653
312/285-1434

Women's Studies Center
535-3 Lucinda
Northern Illinois University
Chicago 60625

Women's Studies Committee
Mundelein College
6363 North Sheridan Road
Chicago 60620

Women's Institute
20 East Jackson, room 902
Chicago 60657
312/922-6749

Women of Northwestern
Ms. Carol Slatkin, Ms. Carol Owen
Northwestern University
Evanston 60201

Prelude
Ms. Vicki Kessler
Knox College
Galesburg 61401

Student Services
College of Lake County
19351 West Washington Street
Grayslake 60030

Women's Center
West Suburban
1 South Park Street
Lombard 60148
312/629-0170

Association of Women Students
Ms. Ayn Crowley
Monmouth College
Monmouth 61462

Greenerfields, Unlimited
Sonja T. Mast, Carol R. Godwin,
Nancy C. Robinson, Katrina Johnson
318 Happ Road
Northfield 60093
312/446-0525

Women's Studies Center
Mary Siegler
Northern Illinois University
540 College View Court
De Kalb 60115
815/752-0110

Kendall College Women's Center
2408 Orrington
Evanston 60201

Women's Liberation Center of Evanston
2214 Ridge Street
Evanston 60201
312/471-4480 (A.M.)

"A Woman's Place"
401 West California
Urbana 61801

INDIANA

Office for Women's Affairs
Indiana University
Memorial Hall—East
Bloomington 47401
812/337-3849

Women's Center
414 North Park
Bloomington 47401
812/366-8691

Continuing Ed. for Women
c/o Janet R. Walker
University of Evansville
Box 329
Evansville 47701

Span Plan
Cecilia Zissis, Director
Purdue University
Office of Dean of Women
Lafayette 47907

South Bend Women's Center
1125 Thomas Street
South Bend 46625

Purdue Women's Caucus
Joyce Field, Corres. Sec.
Purdue University
Krannert Graduate School of
Industrial Administration
West Lafayette 47906
317/463-1736

IOWA

Dean of Women's Office
Anne Doolin
Mt. Mercy College
1330 Elmhurst Drive N.E.
Cedar Rapids 52402

Cont. Ed. for Women Sect.
Betty Durden, Vice-Chairman
Drake University
Des Moines 50311

Women's Information Center
YWCA
8th and Grand
Des Moines 50309
515/244-8961

University of Iowa Women's Center
3 East Market Street
Iowa City 52240
515/353-6265

Women's Committee
Barbara Fassler, Director
Central College
Pella 50219

KANSAS

Lawrence Women's Center
University of Kansas
1314 Oread
Lawrence 66044

**University of Kansas Commission
on the Status of Women**
Dean of Women's Office
Lawrence 66044

Women's Resource Center
Kansas State University
Manhattan 66506

A.W.A.R.E.
Wichita State University
Wichita 67208

KENTUCKY

Women's Center Director
Brescia College, Lafiat Hall
120 West 7th Street
Owensboro 42301

Lexington Women's Center
120 Kentucky Avenue
Lexington 40502

LOUISIANA

New Orleans Women's Center
1422 Felicity Street
New Orleans 70130

Women's Liberation Center
P.O. Box 19001
New Orleans 70119

MAINE

Women's Center
University of Maine—Augusta
University Heights
Augusta 04330

Women's Center
Box 914
Bangor 04401

Brunswick/Bath Women's Center
136 Main Street
Brunswick 04011

MARYLAND

Woman Center
Susan Dubrow
University of Maryland
9010 Riggs Road, Apt. 205
Adelphi 20783

Baltimore Women's Liberation
101 East 25th Street, Suite B2
Baltimore 21218
301/366-6475

Continuing Education for Women
Morgan State College
Baltimore 21239

Women's Center
Towson State College
Box 2013
Baltimore 21204

Women's Center
Essex Community College
P.O. Box 9596
Baltimore 21237

Women's Center
Johns Hopkins University
Box 1134, Levering Hall
Baltimore 21218
301/235-3637 or 336-3300, ext. 529

Women's Center
St. Mary's College of Maryland
Baltimore 21210

Women's Law Center
P.O. Box 1934
Baltimore 21203
301/547-1653

Women's Union
University of Md., Baltimore County
5401 Wilkens Avenue
Baltimore 21203
301/455-2446

Women's Center
Catonsville Community College
800 South Rolling Road
Catonsville 21228
301/747-3220, ext. 355

Women's Center
University of Maryland
1127 Student Union
College Park 20742
301/454-5411

Women's Information Center
4110 School of Library &
    Information Services
College Park 20742
301/454-5441

Women's Resource Center
Valerie Kitch
8905 Footed Ridge
Columbia 21045
301/454-5411

Women's Center
c/o Judy Gray & Nancy Hume
Essex Community College
Room 17, Red Temporaries
Essex 21221
301/682-6000

Women's Center
Carol Blimline, Counselor
Montgomery College
Rockville 20830

St. Mary's Women's Center
Nancy Schniedewind
St. Mary's College
St. Mary's City 20686

Towson Women's Center
Annette Plower, English Department
Towson State College
Baltimore 21204
301/823-7500, ext. 826

Women's Center
Goucher College
Box 1434
Towson 21204

GYN Clinic
Western Maryland College
Westminster 21157

MASSACHUSETTS

Men's Center
Jones Library
Amherst 01002

Southwest Women's Center
University of Massachusetts
John Quincy Adams Lobby
Amherst 01002

Third World Women's Center
University of Massachusetts
Amherst 01002

The Women's Caucus
University of Massachusetts
School of Education
Amherst 01002

Everywoman's Center
Pat Sackrey
University of Massachusetts
Munson Hall, Room A
Amherst 01002
413/545-0883

Southwest Women's Centre
Judith Katz
Southwest, University of Massachusetts
c/o Washington Lobby
Amherst 01002
413/545-0626

Andover Women's Center
224 Lowell Street
Andover 01810

Women's Opportunity Research Center
Middlesex Community College
Div. of Continuing Ed.
Springs Road
Bedford 01730

Boston U. Female Liberation
George Sherman Union
775 Commonwealth
Boston 02215

Boston University Women's Center
Sue McKeon
211 Bay State Road
Boston 02215
617/353-4240

Pregnancy Counseling Service of Boston
3 Joy Street
Boston 02108

Women's Center
Boston State College
174 Ipswich Street
Boston 02115

Women's Center
P.O. Box 286
Prudential Center
Boston 02199

Women's Center
Simmons College
300 The Fenway
Boston 02115

Female Liberation
639 Massachusetts Avenue
Cambridge 02139

Library Collective
492 Putnam Avenue
Cambridge 02139

Radcliffe Institute
Alice K. Smith, Dean
Radcliffe College
3 James Street
Cambridge 02138
617/495-8211

Women and Work
Dr. Mary Potter Rowe
Massachusetts Institute of Technology
Cambridge 02139

Women's Center
46 Pleasant Street
Cambridge 02139
617/354-8807

Women's Research Center
123 Mt. Auburn
Cambridge 02139

Women's Center
Ms. Margaret Fletcher
Bristol Community College
64 Durfee Street
Fall River 02720

Simon's Rock Early College
Great Barrington 01230

Community Women's Center
Rebecca Winburn
208-310 Main Street
Greenfield 01301
413/773-7519

Greenfield Women's Center
Federal Street
Greenfield 01301

Women's Caucus
Janet Levine, Coordinator
1 Kennedy Drive
Hadley 01035

Lowell Women's Center
Lowell YWCA
50 Elm Street
Lowell 01852
617/445-5405

Continuing Education for Women
Suzanne Lipsky, Office of the Dean
Jackson College
Tufts University
Medford 02155

YWCA Women's Resource Center
2nd Floor Recreation Room
Sears Roebuck & Co.
Natick Mall
Natick 01760

New Bedford Women's Center
241 Reed Street
New Bedford 02747

Women's Resource Center
Andover-Newton Theological School
215 Herrick Road
Newton Centre 02159

Southeastern Mass. U. Women's Center
Southeastern Mass. U.
North Dartmouth 02747
617/997-9321, ext. 698

Sophia Sisters: Smith College
  Lesbian Liberation
Annie Korn
Clark House, Smith College
Northampton 01060

Valley Women's Center
Cheryl Schaffer
200 Main Street
Northampton 01060
413/586-2011

Women's Center
6 Goswald Street
Provincetown 02675
617/487-0387

Ann Klemel, Dean of Women
Eastern Nazarene College
23 East Elm
Quincy 02170

North Shore Women Center
Pat Watson
58 High Street
Rockport 01966

Women's Center
Salem State College
Salem 01970

Somerville Women's Health Project
326 Somerville Avenue
Somerville 02143

Women's Center
Mt. Holyoke College
3 Brigham
South Hadley 01075

Women's Health Counseling Service
115 State Street
Springfield 01103

Springfield Women's Center
451 State Street
Springfield 01101
413/732-7113

Brandeis University Women's Center
Rona Shribman
20 Stanley Road
Swampscott 01907
617/598-2188

Lowell Women's Center
Ruth Yaw
90 10th Street
Tewksbury 01876

Women's Center
Clark University
Worcester 01610

Worcester Pregnancy Counseling
52 Burncoat Street
Worcester 01603

Worcester Women's Center
905 Main Street
Worcester 01610
617/753-9622

Worcester Women's Resource Center
Worcester YWCA
2 Washington Street
Worcester 01608
716/791-3181

MICHIGAN
Office of Women's Programs
Barbara Zikmund, Co-director
Albion College
Albion 49224

Center for Continuing Education
Jean Campbell, Director
University of Michigan
330 Thompson Street
Ann Arbor 48108

Feminist House
225 East Liberty, Room 203
Ann Arbor 48104

Gay Advocate Office
Michigan Union
530 South State
Ann Arbor 48104
313/763-4186

Women's Resource Center
Kellogg Community College Library
Battle Creek 49016

The Women's Center
Lake Michigan College
Benton Harbor 49022

Alternative Resource Center
c/o Mandella
16261 Petoskey
Detroit 48221

Detroit Women's Liberation
415 Brainard
Detroit 48201

Women's Action and Aid Center
103 West Alexandrine
Detroit 48201

East Lansing Women's Center
223½ East Grand River
East Lansing 48823

ENCORE Program
Aquinas College
Grand Rapids 49506

Women's Resource Center
June Mochizuki, Director CEW
Western Michigan University
Kalamazoo 49001

Women's Center for Continuing Education
Northern Michigan University
Marquette 49855

Continuum Center for Women
Eleanor Driver, Director
Continuing Education Division
Oakland University
Rochester 48063

Chrysallis Center
Dr. Margaret Cappone, Director
Saginaw Valley College
University Center 48710

Women's Center
Delta College
University Center 48710

Bette C. White, Assistant Dean of Students
East Michigan University
Ypsilanti 48197

MINNESOTA
Duluth Women's Center
University of Duluth Medical School
EPIC—Room 5
Duluth 55812

Woman to Woman Center
University of Minnesota
101 Kirby Student Center
Duluth 55812

Grace High School Women's Center
1350 Gardena Avenue N.E.
Fredley 55432

Mankato Women's Center
c/o Vivian
Mankato State College
426½ North 4th Street
Mankato 56001

Lesbian Resource Center
710 West 22nd Street
Minneapolis 55405
612/374-2345

Minnesota Women's Center
Anne Truax, Director
University of Minnesota
306 Walter Library
Minneapolis 55455

Women's Clearinghouse
c/o Experimental College
1507 University Avenue, S.E.
Minneapolis 55414
612/376-7449

Women's Counseling Service
621 West Lake Street
Minneapolis 55408

Women's Center
c/o Joletta Crooks
Concordia College
Moorhead 56560

St. Olaf Women's Resource Lounge
St. Olaf College
Northfield 55057

MISSISSIPPI

Gay Counseling & Ed. Projects, Anne de Bary
Mississippi Gay Alliance
Box 4470, Mississippi State Union
State College 39762

Women's Action Movement
Mississippi State University
Box 1328
State College 39762

MISSOURI

CEW
Margot Patterson, Coordinator
University of Missouri
Coop. Extension Services
Carthage 64836

Women's Center
501 East Rollins
Columbia 65201

Women's Liberation Union
5138 Tracy
Kansas City 64110

Women's Resource Service
University of Missouri
Division for Continuing Education
1020 East 63rd Street
Kansas City 64110

Women's Resource Center
Esther M. Edwards
William Jewel College
Liberty 64068

CEW
Mrs. Jean M. Pennington
Washington University
Box 1095
St. Louis 63130

St. Louis University Women's Center
Hussleip Hall
3801 West Pine
St. Louis 63108

St. Louis Women's Center
Margaret C. Fagin, CEW Director
University of Missouri
8001 Natural Bridge Road
St. Louis 63121

St. Louis Women's Center
1411 Locust Street
St. Louis 63103

Women's Center
c/o Ms. Helen Dieterich
Florissant Valley Community College
3400 Pershall Road
St. Louis 63135

MONTANA

Women's Action Center
Venture Center
University of Montana
Missoula 59801

NEBRASKA

Women's Study Group
Dr. Evelyn Haller
Doane College, New Dorm 108
Crete 68333
402/826-2161

Women's Resource Center—Lincoln
Room 116, Nebraska Union
14 & R Streets
Lincoln 68506

NEVADA

Women's Resource Center
University of Nevada
Reno 89507

NEW HAMPSHIRE

Concord Women's Center
130 North Main Street
Concord 03103

Franconia Women's Center
Franconia College
Franconia 03580
603/823-8460

Women's Center of the Upper Valley
19 South Main Street
Hanover 03755
603/643-5981

Laconia Women's Center
c/o Carol Pierce
21 Shore Drive
Laconia 03246

Manchester Women's Center
Unitarian Church
Myrtle and Union Streets
Manchester 03106

The Women's Center
104 Middle Street
Manchester 03102

Women's Center
Northampton

Women's Center
c/o Lissi Savin
Box 172
Warner 03278

NEW JERSEY

YWCA Women's Center
Upsala College
Administration Annex 11
East Orange 07019
201/266-7213

Together
7 State Street
Glassboro 08028

Women's Center of Bergen County
166 Main Street
Hackensack 07601
201/342-8958

Middlesex County NOW
Box 94
Iselin 08830

Women's Center
N. Klein, Director
Brookdale Community College
Newman Springs Road
Lincroft 07738

Center for Women's Studies
Dr. Mara M. Vamos
Fairleigh Dickinson University
285 Madison Avenue
Madison 07940
201/377-4700 ext. 369

Drew Women's Collective
c/o Diana Stewart
Drew University
Madison 07940

AWE Women's Center
c/o Ethel Smyth
P.O. Box 583
Maple Wood 07040
201/467-1422

Women's Center
15 West Main Street
Moorestown 08057
609/235-9297

Women's Center
Montclair—North Essex YWCA
159 Glenridge Avenue
Montclair 07042

Ctr. for the American Woman and Politics
Rutgers, The State University
Eagleton Institute of Politics
New Brunswick 08901
201/247-1766, ext. 1384

Women's Center
Douglass College
New Brunswick 08903

Women's Center of New Brunswick
2 Easton Avenue
New Brunswick 08901
201/246-9637

Monmouth County NOW
11 Aberdeen Terrace
New Monmouth 07748
201/671-3123

YWCA Women's Center of the Oranges
395 Main Street
Orange 07052
201/674-1111

Morristown Area NOW
Elizabeth C. Cieri
3379 Route 46, Apt. 16-E
Parsippany 07054
201/334-6135

Princeton Seminary Women's Center
Ms. Martha Bellinger
Princeton Theological Seminary
Princeton 08540

Woman's Place
14½ Witherspoon Street
Princeton 08540
609/924-8989

Somerset County NOW
147 Stony Brook Road
Somerville, N.J. 08876
201/722-3866

Summit NOW
34 Canoe Brook Parkway
Summit 07901
201/277-0135

EVE
Betsy Brown, Director
Kean College
Kean Building
Union 07083

Women's Center
Dr. Constance Waller, Director
Montclair State College
Upper Montclair 07405
201/893-5106

Passaic County NOW
P.O. Box 1051 Valley Station
Wayne 07470
201/274-5042

Women's Center
Viola Wilbanks
Tombrock College
West Patterson 07424

NEW MEXICO

Albuquerque Women's Center
University of New Mexico
1824 Las Lomas
Albuquerque 87106
505/277-3716

Santa Fe Women's Liberation
c/o Guin Reyes
Santa Fe 87501
505/982-1225

NEW YORK

Astoria Women's Center
44-03 28th Avenue
Astoria 11102
212/932-5130

The Women's Research & Resource Center
Dr. Elinor Pam
Queensborough Community College
222-03 Garland Drive
Bayside 11364
212/423-0666

Women's Center
Sarah Lawrence College
Bronxville 10708

The Women's Center
Lehman College, CUNY
2468 Jerome Avenue
Fordham Center
Bronx 10468

Women's Center
c/o Lois Chafee
915 Washington Avenue
Brooklyn 11225

Women's Studies College
SUNY, Buffalo
108 Winspear Road
Buffalo 14214
716/831-3405

Kirkland College Women's Center
Kirkland College
Clinton 13323

Women's Information Center
P.O. Box 268
Dewitt 13224

Queens Women's Center
153-11 61 Road
Flushing 11367

Hofstra Women's Center
Hofstra University
Room 106, Phillips Hall
Hempstead 11550

Women's Center—Nassau County
14 West Columbia Street
Hempstead 11550

Hewlett Women's Center
1007 Broadway
Hewlett 11557

Ithaca Women's Center
140 West State Street
2nd Floor
Ithaca 14850

Women's Center
Cornell University
Willard Straight Hall
Ithaca 14850

Women's Studies Program
Jennie Farley, Director
Cornell University
431 White Hall
Ithaca 14850

Women's Center—Islip
1 Grant Avenue, Off Main Street
Islip 11751
516/581-2680

AIR Gallery
97 Wooster Street
New York 10012

Barnard Women's Center
Jane S. Gould, Director
Barnard College
606 West 120th Street
New York, N.Y. 10027

Career Information Center
c/o Dolores Kaminski
Baruch College, CUNY
17 Lexington Avenue
New York 10010

N.Y. Theological Seminary
    Women's Center
Ms. Payne
235 East 49th Street
New York 10017

N.Y. Women's Center
36 West 22nd Street
New York 10010

N.Y. Women's Law Center
351 Broadway
New York 10013
212/431-4074

NOW Center
47 East 19th Street
New York 10003

Resource Center on Women
Dr. Claire Fulcher
YWCA
600 Lexington Avenue
New York 10022
212/753-4700

Upper East Side Women's Center
c/o Carol Hardin
359 East 68th Street
New York 10021

West Side Woman's Center
210 West 82nd Street
New York 11024

Women's Center
N.Y.C. Firehouse
243 West 20th Street
New York 10011
212/255-9802

Women's Center for Occupation
    and Educational Development
167 East 67th Street
New York 10021
212/861-0931

Women's Inter-Arts Center
549 West 52nd Street
New York 10019
212/246-6570

Women Photographers
The Midtown Y Gallery
Midtown YM-YWHA
344 East 14th Street
New York 10018

Northport Women's Center (Suffolk)
144 Bayview Avenue
Northport 11768
516/757-6564

Women's Information Center
Old Westbury
Oyster Bay 11771

Mid-Hudson Women's Center
27 Franklin Street
Poughkeepsie 12601
914/473-1538

Poughkeepsie Women's Center
96 Market Street
Poughkeepsie 12601
914/454-9487

Rockland City Women's Liberation
    Women's Center
St. Stephen's Episcopal Church
Pierce Hwy. & Eberhardt Road
Pearl River 10965
914/354-7442

Rochester Women's Center
139 Raleigh Street
Rochester 14620

Suffolk Comm. College Women's Group
533 College Road
Selden 11784

Staten Island Women's Center
121 Van Duzen Street
Staten Island 10301

Women's Center
SUNY at Stony Brook
Stony Brook 11790

Women's Center for Continuing Ed.
University College
610 East Fayette Street
Syracuse 13202

Women's Information Center
104 Avondale Place
Syracuse 13210

Women's Center—Academic Center
Sister Margaret Farrara, Dean of Students
Elizabeth Seton College
1061 North Broadway
Yonkers 10701

NORTH CAROLINA

Female Liberation
Box 954
Chapel Hill 27514

Women's Center
1616 Lyndhurst Road
Charlotte 28203
704/334-9655

Disadvantaged Women in Higher Ed.
1 Incinerator Road
Durham 23824

Women's Center
Guilford College Campus
Greensboro 27410

Women's Center
Vicki J. Tolston
Chowan College
Murfreesboro 27855

NORTH DAKOTA
None Reported

OHIO

Continuing Education Group
University of Cincinnati—
    Raymond Walters College
Cincinnati 45236

Educational Resource and Women's Center
c/o Dean of Women
Xavier University
Cincinnati 45207

University of Cincinnati Women's Center
412 Tuc Woman Affairs Council
Cincinnati 45221

Women's Center
c/o Martha Brown
6728 Alpine Avenue
Cincinnati 45236

Women's Center
Case Western Reserve University
Thwing Study Center
11111 Euclid Avenue
Cleveland 44118

Cleveland Women's Center
P.O. Box 2526
East Cleveland 44112

Columbus Women's Liberation
Lutheran Student Center
38 East 12th Avenue
Columbus 43201

Dayton Women's Center
1203 Salem Avenue
Dayton 45406

Office of Special Programs for Women
c/o Ms. Verna Graves, Coordinator
Wright State University
Dayton 45431

Women's Center
University of Dayton
Box 612
Dayton 45469

Women's Center
c/o Ms. Betty Kirschner
Kent State University
Kent Women's Project
Kent 44242

Women's Center
Oberlin College
Wilder Hall
Oberlin 44074

AWS Women's Resource Center
Anne Bush
Miami University
225 Warfield Hall
Oxford 45056

Miami University Women's Information Center
Miami University
Box 123, Bishop Hall
Oxford 45056

Women's Liberation—USN Center
410 East High
Oxford 45406

Women's Center
Linda J. Headrich
Wittenberg University
966 Pythian Avenue
Springfield 45504

Women's Programs
M. Jean Parke, Consultant
The University of Toledo
2801 West Bancroft Street
Toledo 43606

Antioch College Women's Center
Antioch College
Yellow Springs 45387
513/767-7331, ext. 311

OKLAHOMA

Women's Resource Center
University of Tulsa
600 South College
Tulsa 74104

OREGON

Office of Women's Studies
c/o Dr. Jeanne Dost
Oregon State University
Corvallis 97331

The George House
c/o Mrs. Laura Crockett
Western Baptist Seminary
5511 S.E. Hawthorne
Portland 97215

Women's Institute and Resource Center
Portland State University
Portland 97207

Women's Research & Study Center
University of Oregon
c/o Sociology Department, Joan Acker
Eugene 97403
503/686-5002

PENNSYLVANIA

Career-Counseling Center for Adult Women
JoAnne Painter, Director
Villa Maria College
2551 West Lake Road
Erie 16505

Women's Center
230 West Chestnut Street, First Floor
Lancaster 17603

Bucks County Community College Women's Caucus
c/o Marlene Miller
Hicks Art Center
BCCC
Newton 18940

Continuing Education for Women
Jean McBryde Swanson, Coordinator
Temple University
Mitten Hall, Room 207
Philadelphia 19122

Women's Center
Cathy Balsley, Coordinator
Temple University
Mitten Hall, First Floor
Philadelphia 19122
215/787-7990

Center for Women in Medicine
Nina B. Woodside, Director
Medical College of Pennsylvania
3300 Henry Avenue
Philadelphia 19129
215/849-0400

Philadelphia Women's Liberation Center
P.O. Box 19826
Philadelphia 19143

Women's Center
Sharon Grossman, Coordinator
University of Pennsylvania
3533 Locust Walk
Philadelphia 19104

Women's Center
4634 Chester Avenue
Philadelphia 19104
215/729-2001

Women's Resource Center
YWCA Philadelphia
Kensington Branch
174 West Allegheny Avenue
Philadelphia

Women's Center
Community College of Allegheny County
Allegheny Campus
Pittsburgh 15212

Women's Liberation House
Penn. State University
245 East Hamilton Avenue
State College 16801

Swarthmore Gay Liberation
c/o Christina Crosby
Swarthmore College
Swarthmore 19081

RHODE ISLAND

Kingston Women's Liberation
University of Rhode Island
Memorial Union
Kingston 02881

Resource Center for Women in Higher Education
Dr. Jacquiline Mattfeld, Director
Brown University
Providence 02912

Women's Liberation Umbrella
59 Olive Street
Providence 02906

**Women's Liberation Union of
Rhode Island**
Box 2302, East Side Station
Providence 02906

YWCA Women's Center
Jackson Street
Providence 02903

SOUTH CAROLINA
Women's Center
1106 Hagwood Avenue
Columbia 29205

Women's Center
Winthrop College
Winthrop Coalition Group
P.O. Box 6763
Rock Hill 29730

SOUTH DAKOTA
None Reported

TENNESSEE
Nashville Tennessee Women's Center
1112 19th Avenue South
Nashville 37212
615/327-1969

Women's House
The University of the South
Sewanee 37375

TEXAS
Women's Liberation
1106 West 22nd Street
Austin 78705

Austin Women's Center
1208 Baylor Street
West Austin 78103

Women's Center
Sandra I. Tinkham, Director
3118 Fondrell Drive
Dallas 75205

Women's Center
c/o Office of the Dean of
Student Programs
Southern Methodist University
Dallas 75275

Women for Change Center
20001 Bryan Tower, Suite 290
Dallas 75201
214/741-2391

Women's Center
North Texas State University
Denton 76203

Women's Resource Center
YWCA of Houston
1521 Texas Avenue
Houston 77002

Women's Center
3602 Milam
Houston 77002

UTAH
Women's Environ Institute
Jan W. Tyler, Director and
Dean of Women
Weber State College
Harrison Boulevard
Ogden 84403
801/399-5941

Women's Center
Brigham Young University
Provo 84601

Women's Resource Center
Shauna M. Adix, Director
University of Utah
293 Union Building
Salt Lake City 84112
801/581-8030

VERMONT
Women's Center
217 North Winooski
Burlington 05404

Women's Union
Lisa DeMauro, Chairperson
Middlebury College
Middlebury 05753

Feminist Studies
Goddard College
Aiken Dorm
Plainfield 05667
802/454-8311, ext. 273

Women's Center
Ellen Dorsh/Mary Boyle, Directors
Windham College
Putney 05346

VIRGINIA
None Reported

WASHINGTON
Women's Center
c/o Mary Robinson
Women's Commission & Occupational
Resource Center
Western Washington State College
Bellingham 98225

Lesbian Resource Center
YWCA
4224 University Way N.E.
Seattle 98105
206/632-4747, ext. 3

**Seattle Counseling Center for
Sexual Minorities**
1720 16th Avenue
Seattle 98134
206/329-8737 or 329-8707

Women's Center
University of Washington
Seattle 98195

Women's Guidance Center
Alene H. Moris, Director
1209 N.E. 41st Street
Seattle 98195

Tacoma Women's Center
c/o Debbie Jordan
1108 North Fife Street
Tacoma 98406

Women's Center
Chris Smith, Director
University of Puget Sound
Tacoma 98416

Women's Center
Tacoma Community College
Tacoma 98465

Women's Center
c/o Hallien Johnson
Office of Women's Programs
Spokane Falls Community College
West 3410 Fort George Wright Drive
Spokane 99204

Women's Center
Marcia Weidig
Whitman College
Walla Walla 99362

WEST VIRGINIA
Women's Center
Beckley College
South Kanawha Street
Beckley 25801

Women's Center
Appalachian Bible Institute
Bradley 25818

Women's Information Center
West Virginia University
Bennett House
121 Wiley Street
Morgantown 26506

WISCONSIN
Women's Action Group
Ms. Joan Smith
Northland College
Ashland 54806

Women's Center
University of Wisconsin
Green Bay 54302

**Center for Women's and
Family Living Education**
430 Lowell Hall
610 Langdon Street
Madison 53706

Scarlett Letter Collective
University of Wisconsin YWCA
306 North Brooks
Madison 53715

Women's Center
836 East Johnson
Madison 53703

Research Center on Women
Kathleen C. Gigle, Coordinator
Alverno College
3401 South 39th Street
Milwaukee 53215
414/671-5400

The Women's Center
2110 West Wells Street
Milwaukee 53208

Women's Center
North Urella Street
Milwaukee

The Women's Coalition
Ellen Guiseppi
2211 East Kenwood Blvd.
Milwaukee 53211
414/964-7535

Women's Information Center
University of Wisconsin-Milwaukee
Box 189
Milwaukee 53201

Oshkosh Women's Center
Wisconsin State University
Oshkosh Student Association
Oshkosh 54900

Women's Center
University of Wisconsin-Oshkosh
312 Dempsey Hall
Oshkosh 54901

WYOMING
None Reported

Photo credits

Cover Read photo strips from left to right and each strip from top to bottom.

Ann Phillips
Hugh Rogers from Monkmeyer Press
Shalom Bernstein from Monkmeyer Press
Mimi Forsyth from Monkmeyer Press

Sybil Shelton from Monkmeyer Press
Hugh Rogers from Monkmeyer Press
Mimi Forsyth from Monkmeyer Press

Donald Miller from Monkmeyer Press
Mimi Forsyth from Monkmeyer Press
Michal Heron from Monkmeyer Press

Mimi Forsyth from Monkmeyer Press
Ann Phillips
Mimi Forsyth from Monkmeyer Press

Page 20 Anne Marsden

Page 60-61 Authors

Page 66 Ann Phillips

Page 70 Lawrence D. Thornton

Page 73 Top: Hugh Rogers from Monkmeyer Press
Bottom left: Lowber Tiers from Monkmeyer Press
Bottom right: Ann Phillips

Page 78 H. Armstrong Roberts

This book was designed by Peter Forstenzer.
It was set in linotype Times Roman at Arvin Typographers, Inc., New York, New York;
and printed and bound by The Lane Press, Inc., Burlington, Vermont.